DEVON AND CORNWALL RECORD SOCIETY

New Series, Vol. 31

Names of Ships with
remarks on them & by whom
composed. — 1817 —

N° 1817
1 Sloop called Heroine of 111 18/94 Ton but not built at
Topsham, too circular a body would role in
a sea very much but good proportions only rather
too sharp & sailes very fast — should not like to
compose by her but if did would make her
carry her flatness much farther aft

N° 1817
2 Sloop called Partunda (a Brixham trawl-
-boat) of 37 Ton 4/94 which answered very well &
sailed remarkably fast a good Draught to
compose such a Vessel by

N° 1817
3 — Brig called Tutoress of 211 Ton 25/94 composed by
D B Davy — her stern too heavy, main breadth
not quite high enough, say 2 or 2½ higher
would make her look better, & her flatness

Frontispiece. 'Names of ships with remarks on them & by whom composed, 1817': a page from Daniel Bishop Davy's Memoranda Book. Text p. 1. Photograph by C. N. Ponsford.

DEVON & CORNWALL RECORD SOCIETY

New Series, Vol. 31

SHIPBUILDING

ON THE EXE

The Memoranda Book of
DANIEL BISHOP DAVY
(1799–1874)
OF TOPSHAM, DEVON

With a biography of Robert Davy (1762–1862)

Edited with an Introduction by

CLIVE N. PONSFORD

1988

ISBN 0 901853 31 3

Printed for the Society by
A. Wheaton and Company Ltd.
EXETER
ENGLAND

CONTENTS

LIST OF ILLUSTRATIONS

LIST OF TABLES

LIST OF PLANS

INTRODUCTION

The compiler of these memoranda, Daniel Bishop Davy (1799–1874), lived and worked at Topsham on the tidal reaches of the river Exe between Exeter and the sea. He was the son of Robert Davy, builder of the famous polar discovery vessel H.M.S. *Terror*, and was a young man still in his teens whe he made the first entries in 1817 in a stout, parchment-bound volume, in outward appearance not unlike a ship's log-book. He had clearly received a considerable amount of instruction in his father's shipyards – at Gulpit, Countess Wear, and at Passage, Topsham – and perhaps elsewhere, and was already able to design or 'compose' brigs and other sailing vessels. He was familiar with the numerous technical terms peculiar to the art of shipbuilding and was acquiring a knowledge of costs and materials. He was also observant and his remarks on the different vessels with which he was associated are valuable in that they show how, through a series of small modifications, successful designs were gradually perfected.

Davy provides detailed information about shipbuilding on the Exe and on other businesses in which the family were engaged, such as the timber trade, lime-burning and anchor chainmaking. He also records his coastal travels or voyages and tells us that in September 1818 he visited Greenock, on the river Clyde in Scotland. While there he made notes about three ships that had recently been launched, one by Robert Steele and the other two by John Scott & Sons. He states that they were fine ships, 'faithfully built & fastened' (text, p. 13). The following December he set off along the South Coast, gathering information in Dorset and Hampshire about the building of ships and the size and quality of the timber used in their construction; but this time he was not so impressed, for he observed that in one shipyard the plank on a brig was very badly fastened and that two smacks had 'very small bad sappy frames'. He did record, however, that the vessels built by Mr Good at Bridport were almost as strongly framed as those built by his father and himself: 'All Mr G'ds scantlings are nearly equal to *ours*', he noted in an aside that suggests he was proud of the sturdy vessels built on the Exe (text, p. 14).

In 1819 he went by sea to the East Coast, having previously drawn up lists of shipbuilders, tanners and timber agents and merchants, and he records (text, pp. 15–21) his attempts to sell elm keel pieces and oak timber. He took samples with him and invited builders to come aboard his ship to inspect them; but the experience was rather like carrying the proverbial coals to Newcastle – his final port of call – and he achieved little success, except from an unexpected quarter, a firm of coachbuilders indicating that they would buy 'elm board, spokes, nail stocks &c' provided they liked the sample that was sent to them. His comments on some of the hard-headed men of Yorkshire and the North East and the difficulties of doing business with them add spice to this section of the manuscript. Davy continued to make entries in the book, at times spasmodically, until 1827, but then laid it aside before, eventually, picking it up again to list (text, pp. 58–60) the hundred or so vessels built both by Robert Davy and himself, the last of which, the brigantine *Clitus* and the ketch *Samson*, were both registered on 17 October 1843.[1]

The original manuscript volume is now in the library of Topsham Museum at Holman House, 25 The Strand. It was given by a visitor to the late Miss Dorothy Holman, the museum's founder, and was formerly displayed in a showcase, where the editor first saw it in the late 1970s. The donor's name has not been recorded but he or she was probably a member of the Davy family, for the museum also acquired around 1970 a manuscript copy of a biography of Robert Davy written by his youngest son Francis – printed here as Appendix A – and a picture of the 600-ton East Indiaman *Caroline* (later the *Batavia*), the largest ship that he (Robert Davy) built. The Memoranda Book, which is in a good state of preservation, is about 16.75 cm wide, 21 cm deep and 3 cm thick. The leaves are unruled and some are blank. The writer's method of numbering pages is unusual (for example, page 2 is two facing pages); and, having started the book, he turned it about to make further entries on unnumbered pages at the back. Later memoranda were jotted down where there happened to be a gap and, as the book remained in use for a long period, the arrangement of the material became somewhat haphazard. If Davy had published it, he would almost certainly have revised the order of contents, and this has been done to a certain extent in the transcription presented here.

SHIPBUILDING TERMS

Davy's volume poses two main problems for landsmen. First, it is awash with terms used in the theory and practice of shipbuilding. Every part of a wooden sailing vessel built by the Davys – and, of course, by others – had a name. The ribs, for instance, consisted of floor timbers, first foothooks ('futtocks'), second foothooks, thirds and tops, and each one of these components had a siding and moulding dimension which were listed in what was known as the 'scantling' of the frame. There were also 'knightheads', 'bitts', 'whelps', 'coamings', 'carlings', 'catheads', 'sir-marks', 'treenails' and 'deadwood', to mention but a few of the terms found in the manuscript. To explain these a Glossary has been appended to the text, drawn mainly from a shipbuilding treatise published in 1830 by Peter Hedderwick, designer of a number of vessels built by Robert Davy for Scottish owners.

The second problem is that Daniel Davy refers frequently to a set of numbered 'drafts' or plans and gives tables of measurements relating to these; but unfortunately the drafts, which would have shown the shape and form of the vessels, have not been preserved with the book. However, the fact that the Davys worked from drawings is worth noting, since their successors at Topsham, John Holman & Sons, used wooden half-hull models, a collection of which can been seen in the town's museum.[2] As the

---

[1]Devon Record Office, Exeter Customs House, Register of Shipping, Vol. 6 (1838–47): *Clitus* 1843, No. 16; *Samson* 1843, No. 17 – the register records that she was lost off Cape Cornwall on 23 July 1846.

[2]The founder of this firm, John Bagwell Holman, commanded two Davy-built vessels, the *Fortitude* and the *Ebenezer*. For further information see C. N. Ponsford, *Topsham and the Exe Estuary*, Exeter, 1979, or visit Topsham Museum which has numerous items connected with the business.

entry on 'Lines' in the Glossary explains, the main drawings used in marine architecture are three in number: the sheer plan, the half-breadth plan and body plan. For the purpose of these a ship is divided into a fore- and after-body, separated by an imaginary athwartship section at the widest part, called the 'midship bend' or 'dead-flat' and represented, as in this manuscript, by the symbol ⬗. Davy uses the letters of the alphabet – from A to N or from A to O – to distinguish the frames from the dead-flat to the bow, and numbers from 1 up to 22 for the frames from the dead-flat to the stern. From the information given in the section entitled 'Detailed dimensions' (text, pp. 46–57) it should be possible to reconstruct some of the missing plans, the basic dimensions being recorded either in the text or in the editorial notes which are based on the Exeter Customs House registers and other sources.

The word 'ship' is rarely used in the manuscript except to describe a full-rigged ship, such as the Topsham-built *Jamaica Planter*, with three masts and a full complement of square sails on each. Lesser craft, including snows, brigs, schooners, smacks and sloops, were, correctly speaking, vessels; and in this Introduction I have tried to follow Davy on this point.

THE DAVY FAMILY

The Davys' ancestors reputedly came to Devon as fugitives from Dorset after supporting the Duke of Monmouth in his ill-fated rebellion in 1685.[3] They settled in Heavitree parish on the outskirts of Exeter and from there, in the 1760s, moved to Wear (now Countess Wear), on the eastern bank of the Exe, where, besides farming, James Davy (1729–1813) worked various lime-kilns and also ran a coal business. His son Robert (born 1762) later joined him and, from repairing the barges that brought the stone to the kilns, launched out into shipbuilding. The biography (Appendix A) gives a colourful account of Robert Davy's remarkable career. He lived to be nearly a hundred and, in the words of its author, 'it may be truly said that from 1790 to about 1825 he was the largest lime-burner, coal merchant and shipbuilder in the West of England; also he farmed and grazed very extensively; and he did a little in the Newfoundland trade, besides selling large quantities of oak timber and bark &c'.

Plate 2 shows the derelict lime-kilns in the Davy family's first shipyard at Glasshouse, Countess Wear.[4] The yard was in operation in the 1790s. In May 1803 five sailing lighters, built or rebuilt there and belonging to Robert Davy, were registered at Exeter: the *Increase* (built Wear 1796) *Greyhound* (built Wear 1792), *Betsey* (built Wear 1796), and *Lion* and *Tiger* (both built at Topsham in 1783 and rebuilt at Wear in 1799).[5] All five were still owned by Robert Davy when D. B. Davy drew up a list of his shipping property in

---

[3]G.T., 'The Monmouth Rebellion', *Devon & Cornwall Notes & Gleanings*, Vol. 5, 1892, pp. 127–8.

[4]The photograph was taken in 1978; the kilns have since been demolished.

[5]Devon Record Office, Exeter Customs House, Register of Shipping, Vol. 1 (1786–1811), 1803, Nos. 27–31, 20 May.

1822 (text, p. 61). The *Resolution*, a square-sterned sloop with a flush deck, 74³³/₉₄ tons burden, recorded as built at Glasshouse, was registered at Exeter on 9 December 1796, and several much larger vessels were subsequently built in the yard, including the West Indiaman *Grace*, which sailed from the Exe in March 1799 to join a convoy for Jamaica, and the brig *Mary*, built about 1800.[6] Strangely, none of these names is found in D. B. Davy's list of the different merchant ships built by his father.

As the biography of Robert Davy tells us, he gave up shipbuilding at Glasshouse about 1802 and commenced building near the lime-kilns at Gulpit, a little higher up Glasshouse Gut, a narrow channel which branches from the Exe immediately above Countess Wear Bridge and rejoins the river a few hundred yards further downstream (Plate 3). A shipwright named Thomas Bishop took responsibility for some of the vessels built there,[7] including one of the last, the *Exeter* brig, launched in 1818. Gulpit was one of the yards in which Davy built warships;[8] the other was the Passage yard, two miles further down the river at Topsham. The latter took its name from the ferry or passage-boat that crosses the Exe just below the site of the shipyard. Davy had experienced difficulties in getting vessels down from Countess Wear and from 1806 onwards built all the larger ones at Topsham.

In April 1827, when involved in a law case about the navigation of the Exe above Topsham, Robert Davy swore an affidavit, stating 'that within the period of 30 years last past he has carried on the business of a shipbuilder to a considerable extent at & in the neighbourhood of Wear . . . and that in the course of such his business he hath built many vessels for His Majesty's service & for the East & West & other trades of very heavy burthen, among which he . . . enumerated the following: the *Batavia* of 600 tons register, the *Earl St Vincent* between 4 & 500 tons, the *Ann & Segar* between 2 and 300 tons, as may be seen by the respective registers thereof, the *Conflict, Swinger* & *Rapid* gun-brigs & a very considerable number of other vessels for His Majesty's service & private trade'.[9] In another affidavit, sworn the previous month, he stated that he and his father before him had upward of 60 years 'carried on a very considerable trade at Wear' as lime-burners and coal merchants and 'in the carrying on such his trade he is now & hath for many years past been in the habit of conveying upwards of a thousand barges and lighters loads of coals, culm and lime stone to his wharfs & kilns at Wear aforesaid on the navigable river Exe'.[10]

Calculations in Daniel Davy's Memoranda Book reveal that in 1822 Robert Davy was operating lime-kilns at four different locations. The most productive kilns were near his home at Higher Wear; the others were at Gulpit, at a place called Marsh on the river Clyst and at Lympstone (text, pp. 63–4). To serve these he had in that year a fleet of six 'stone boats' and eleven lighters; he also owned coal lighters and two sloops trading to Bristol. In addition he held shares in vessels which he had built, namely the

[6]Robert Davy was part-owner of both the *Resolution* and *Grace*, Exeter Customs House, Register of Shipping, Vol. 1.
[7]He died in 1826. See Appendix B, p. 81
[8]There are Gulpit Cottages in the vicinity still.
[9]Devon Record Office, Exeter City Archives, Law Papers, Box 20, Attorney General & Exeter v Davy, 1827.
[10]Ibid.

West Indiaman *Medina*, the schooner *Ceres* and the 'London traders' *Flower, Hope, Good Intent* and *Fortitude* (text, p. 61). His eldest son Robert was resident in 1852 at Ringwood in Hampshire,[11] but three other sons, Daniel, Samuel and Francis – none of whom seems to have married – assisted in the various family businesses and later took them over after their father was robbed of his eyesight. His sufferings at the hands of eye surgeons are vividly described by Francis Davy who paints an almost biblical image of him when old and blind being guided across his fields by a boy.

Francis also touches on the scale of his father's shipbuilding business, particularly during the Napoleonic Wars which raged from 1803 to 1815. 'At one period,' he states, 'Mr Davy had ships building at one place and the other of various tonnage amounting on the whole to upwards of 1,800 tons.' He completed all of his Royal Navy contracts on time and towards the close of the conflict received large premiums for completing them 'more or less before the time' (text, p. 71). The last two warships that he built, the *Hind* and the *Tyne*, sailed from Exmouth in 1814 (text, p. 79), and from then until 1819 Robert Davy launched about six to eight merchant vessels a year. Some of these were built on speculation, including four vessels advertised for sale in 1816, all of them 'ready for launching' (text, pp. 80–81). Daniel Davy's Memoranda Book provides evidence of a post-war slump, with vessels being built for unrealistic prices. In 1819 he noted that Mr William Gibson of Hull 'has been building a vessel of about 380 tons register which he has had in hand for these last two years & not being able to sell her he now intends fitting her out himself' (text, p. 16). The Davys decided to close their Gulpit shipyard but to continue at Topsham. In 1820 their output fell to four vessels and, over the next 23 years, only a further 14 were built.

However, the family had other irons in the fire and Robson's *Commercial Directory for London and the Western Counties* for 1835 lists Robert Davy and Sons as shipowners, merchants and lime-burners at Countess Wear and D. B. Davy and Company as anchor and cable manufacturers and merchants at Passage, Topsham, in addition to which there was an iron, hemp and tallow business which in 1850 was being run by Francis Davy,[12] and a Topsham coal yard and quay.[13] The family also owned land (text, pp. 65–6) and their properties at Topsham included two tenanted public houses, the Lord Nelson and the Ship.[14]

DANIEL BISHOP DAVY

Daniel Bishop Davy, second son of Robert and his wife Grace (née Bishop), was baptised on 30 June 1799 at Topsham parish church.[15] He learned shipbuilding at an early age and for much of the period covered by his

[11]Will of Robert Davy senior, Summary in Westcountry Studies Library, Exeter, Exeter families file (Davy/Hodder).
[12]William White, *History, Gazetteer and Directory of Devonshire*, Sheffield, 1850, p. 166.
[13]Will of Robert Davy, loc. cit.
[14]Ibid.
[15]H. Tapley-Soper (ed.), *Parish of Topsham, Marriages, Baptisms & Burials, A.D. 1600 to 1837*, Devon and Cornwall Record Society, 1938. All subsequent references to Topsham parish registers are taken from this source.

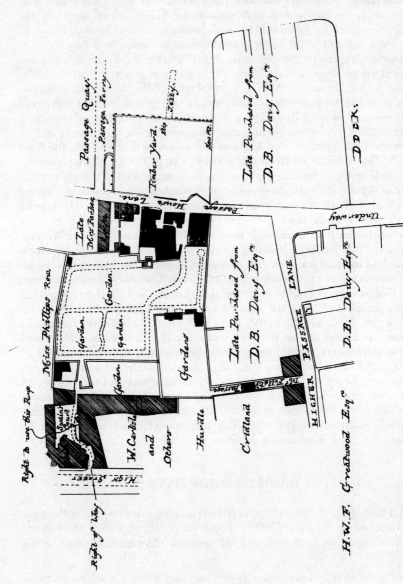

Sketch plan of riverside properties in Topsham north of the Ferry showing some formerly belonging to Daniel Bishop Davy, from a conveyance dated 5 November 1866 between members of the Follett and Holman families. The area bottom right of the plan was the site of Davy's Passage Shipyard. Topsham Museum, Holman Papers, 1/3.

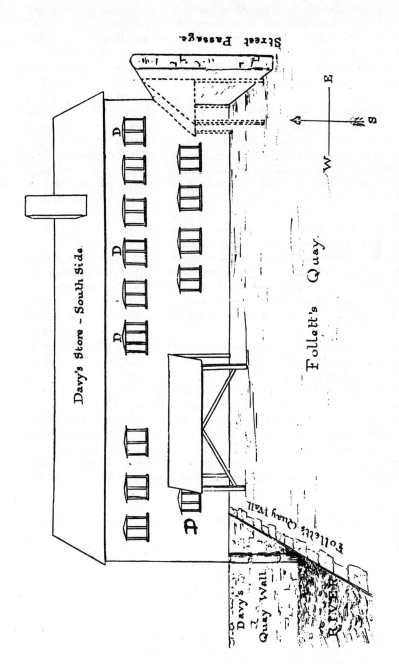

Sketch of Follett's Quay and Davy's Store, from an Agreement dated 17 April 1862 between D. B. Davy and John Follett concerning the enjoyment of certain lights. Topsham Museum, Holman Papers, 1/2.

Memoranda Book was assistant to his father. In 1826 when Daniel was aged 27, Robert gave up the Passage yard to him (text, p. 71) and that year he launched the *Dorothea* and the *Eliza*, both vessels being particularly well documented in the manuscript. Subsequently he owned shares in almost all the vessels that he built – an exception was the schooner *Vansittart* launched in 1834 for Captain John Parker of Exmouth,[16] whose family also owned two other Davy schooners, the *Mary* and the *Britannia* (text, pp. 40–41).

Several paintings have survived in private ownership depicting schooners built by D.B.Davy. The Topsham Museum has a photograph of one of these, showing the *Ebenezer* (Plate 10) at Malta under the command of Captain John Holman, who was later to become prominent as a shipbuilder at Topsham and as a pioneer of marine insurance. Three other pictures show schooners operated by the firm of Cole and Company; these were painted in 1833 by the noted marine artist William John Huggins.[17] One has a small label on the back, identifying the vessel portrayed as the *Ace of Trumps,* built at Topsham by Daniel Bishop Davy for himself and William Cole Cole of the Devon County Bank in Exeter.[18] The other two are not named, but it has been suggested that they are the *Post Boy* and *Racer.* Details of an earlier vessel operated by Cole and Company, the *Exeter,* are given in the Memoranda Book; she was commanded by Captain Henry John Row of London, later master and part-owner of the *Post Boy.* When the latter vessel was first registered at Exeter on 19 July 1831 her owners were: William Cole Dicker of Exeter, banker, with 24 of her 64 shares; Daniel Davy with 16; Henry John Row, master mariner, with 16; and Henry Collins of Exeter, banker, with 8 shares.[19] *Racer,* registered 12 months later,[20] was jointly owned by Cole Dicker and Daniel Davy (32 shares each) and so too was *Ace of Trumps,* registered at Exeter on 25 May 1833,[21] Dicker having changed his name the previous February to William Cole Cole as a condition of inheriting property under the will of his uncle, John Cole of Exeter, one of the founders of the Devon County Bank.[22] There is evidence that *Racer* and *Ace of Trumps* were sometimes used to fetch winter fruit from St. Michael's in the Azores and they were certainly more sleekly built than some of the earlier Davy schooners, as Table 2 shows. The largest vessels that Daniel Davy built, the three-masted barques *Amy* and *Emelyn,*[23] were also jointly owned by their builder and William Cole Cole, as was the

[16]Devon Record Office, Exeter Customs House, Register of Shipping, Vol. 5 (1829–38), 1834, No. 8.

[17]The history of the vessels depicted in these three paintings has been researched in the Public Record Office by Mr Robin Imray, who first drew the editor's attention to the links between Cole and Company and Daniel Bishop Davy.

[18] John Ryton, *Banks and Banknotes of Exeter 1769–1906,* Exeter, 1984, pp. 34–40.

[19]Devon Record Office, Exeter Customs House, Register of Shipping, Vol. 5(1829–38) 1831, No. 15.

[20]Ibid. 1832, No. 20.

[21]Ibid. 1833, No. 14.

[22]Ibid. 1831, No. 15:'The Gazette of 22nd February 1833 authorizes William Cole Dicker of the city of Exeter to use the surname of Cole only instead of that of Dicker' – memo appended to details of schooner *Post Boy.* See also John Ryton, op. cit.

[23]Devon Record Office, Exeter Customs House, Register of Shipping, Vol. 6 (1838–47): 1839, No. 27, *Amy,* 232³⁄₁₀ tons N.M., 223⁴⁹⁄₉₄ tons O.M.: 1841, No. 7, *Emelyn,* 293⁷⁄₁₀ tons N.M., 274⁴⁸⁄₉₄ tons O.M. They were named after William Cole Cole's daughters.

brigantine *Clitus,* launched in 1843, although Cole did not acquire his shares in her until a year after she was built.[24]

The launch of the *Emelyn* in March 1841 must have been one of the high points of D. B. Davy's shipbuilding career. 'Upwards of 2,000 persons' crowded into his yard to watch, and afterwards, as reported in the local press (text, p. 82), 'all the workmen were regaled at Southcott's Nelson Inn with a good substantial dinner'.[25] Other newspaper reports reveal that in August 1845 Daniel and his brothers Francis and Samuel were associated with a proposed Exeter, Topsham and Exmouth Railway. All three were elected to the provisional committee and D. B. Davy was subsequently deputy chairman of the committee of management.[26] The days of the Davy shipbuilding business were now drawing to a close. In April 1846 a full repairing lease was drawn up in which Daniel Bishop Davy agreed to let his shipyard at Topsham on a 14-year term, beginning on June 24 that year, to John Holman, of Topsham, sailmaker, and John Walters, of Exmouth, shipbuilder, for an annual rent of £70. The draft lease mentions

> two shipbuilding slips, lead tank boiler, saw pit, boat shed with steam kiln, block shop and blacksmith's shop, moulding loft and a loft over the same situate in a yard at Topsham aforesaid wherein the said D. B. Davy has for some years past carried on the business of a shipbuilder.

The premises were described as being 'bounded on the north by a dock and quay belonging to [Alexander?] Hamilton Esqr, on the east by a road leading to the town of Topsham, on the south by premises in the occupation of Mr John Follett and on the west by the river Exe'. Also included in the lease was a half-part of Davy's timber field adjoining the Lord Nelson Inn 'and now staked off with two sawpits therein', two houses in Upper Passage Lane (now Follett Road), one of which was occupied by Francis Davy as tenant, and an engine house in the shipyard.[27]

D. B. Davy continued to live nearby and in the 1851 Census was recorded aged 50, as resident at Lower Passage, Topsham, together with two servants, aged 51 and 30. Ten years later he was to be found residing at a fine, new, detached house called Grove Hill, at the head of what is now Station Road, Topsham, and the 1871 Census recorded him as living there in some style with a staff consisting of a housekeeper, cook, housemaid, gardener and general servant. He was described as a magistrate for Devon and Exeter and landowner.[28] His death on 16 August 1874, aged 75, was noticed briefly in the Exeter newspapers and more fully in *Richards's Weekly Advertiser* for Topsham and district (text, p. 82).

POSTSCRIPT: DAVY'S SHIPYARD STEAM ENGINE

An account of Daniel Davy's shipyard steam engine, housed presumably in

[24]Ibid. 1843, No. 16.

[25]*Woolmer's Exeter & Plymouth Gazette,* 13 March 1841.

[26]*Trewman's Exeter Flying-Post,* 14 and 21 August 1845.

[27]Devon Record Office, MS Transcripts of schedules, deeds, extracts &c relating to Topsham properties, Vol. A, pp.41–5.

[28]Westcountry Studies Library, Exeter, Microfilm copies of the Censuses of 1851, 61 and 71.

the engine shed earlier mentioned, was published in 1920 by Hugh Wilson Holman. He stated that it was a late eighteenth century beam engine constructed at the Soho Engineering Works, Birmingham, by Boulton and Watt, from whom it was purchased by a Topsham ropemaker called Follett; D. B. Davy acquired it about 1830 and used it for sawing timber; and about 1860 John Holman set it up in his new shipyard at Strand Dock. It survived until 1913, when H.W. Holman offered it to Exeter Museum, which refused it on the grounds that it had no space. A few years later it was found smashed to pieces.[29]

ASPECTS OF DANIEL DAVY'S MEMORANDA BOOK

Vessels for Scottish owners

One of the more interesting aspects of these memoranda is Daniel Davy's early acquaintanceship with Peter Hedderwick who, from being a ship's carpenter in 1796, became a marine architect, shipbuilder and surveyor. He was also the author of *A Treatise on Marine Architecture*, a detailed and now very scarce book privately printed in Edinburgh in 1830. The particular copy studied for the purposes of this Introduction was located in the Science Museum Library in London, but its accompanying volume of plates, although listed in the catalogue, could not be found. The list of the 181 subscribers to the *Treatise* reads like a Who's Who of British shipbuilding of the period, and the various vessels mentioned within its pages include several built by Davys.

Hedderwick lived at Leith, Edinburgh's port, and it seems probable that he came down to Topsham about the building of 'Scotch smacks' for carrying passengers and goods between Leith and Wapping on the river Thames. These were large, burdensome, single-masted vessels from about 140 to 200 tons. An excellent illustration of one 'getting under-weigh' on the Humber is provided by the Hull marine artist John Ward (Plate 7). In the period 1814–19 Robert Davy built four 'Scotch smacks': the *Czar, Hawk* and *Eagle* for the Edinburgh, Glasgow and Leith Shipping Company and the *Edinburgh Castle* for the Edinburgh and Leith Shipping Company. The author of *Reid's Leith & London Smack Directory*, a booklet published in 1819,[30] states that four companies were engaged in the trade, employing a total of 27 sailing vessels, the largest of which was the Topsham-built *Eagle*, 196 tons. He goes on to say that the crews, including master, mate and steward, were usually fourteen in number, and that in the eighteenth century brigs were used on the route, but

their construction and accommodation were, comparatively speaking, bad, having only one cabin, and that very small: they were so bulky, that it was difficult to fill them with goods, and as they waited till they were full, or nearly so, the time of their sailing was extremely uncertain; hence, many persons preferred going by the smacks, which sailed from Berwick

---

[29] *Devon & Cornwall Notes and Queries*, Vol. XI (1920–21), p. 59.

[30] Printed and sold by William Reid, Leith. It has about 23 pages and a chart. The distance from London Bridge to Leith Harbour is stated to be 429¼ miles and 192 miles per day was considered very good sailing, although a passage had been made in 42 hours.

to London with salmon;[31] the owners of which, finding the trade advantageous, about the year 1791, sent them to Leith for goods and passengers, and they called at Berwick for the fish on their passage up [to London]. From the success which attended that mode of conveyance, some enterprising merchants in Leith, resolved to try, whether it would not answer, to have the same sort of vessels in the trade direct between Leith and London. This excellent plan was first set on foot in the year 1802, under the name of the Edinburgh and Leith Shipping Company, and it has succeeded so well, that there are now three additional companies . . .

The 27 vessels listed in the directory include the four built by Robert Davy, 16 built at Bridport, three built at Leith, three at Berwick and one at 'Blythe'.[32] The *Edinburgh Castle*, D.B.Davy tells us, was 'drawn by Mr P. Hedderwick' who in his *Treatise* includes a plan of a Leith smack of 173 tons, similar in appearance to that illustrated in the lithograph by John Ward. These vessels had a big spread of canvas including a gaff-rigged mainsail and one or more squaresails and studding sails; the smack in the background of Ward's drawing can be seen hoisting her main yard, with a man in the rigging. The main boom of the Leith smack depicted by Hedderwick was 66 ft and the bowsprit projected 38 ft outside the stem.[33] Hedderwick noted that the *Edinburgh Castle* was 'a fine sea-boat and sails fast', and that the *Eagle* 'sails fair: very fast in light winds'. The latter was used to test a double-acting pump, for which Hedderwick received twenty guineas and a silver medal from the Society of Arts and Commerce.[34] The 'Scotch smacks' were later replaced with steamers on the London to Leith route and some of them,[35] including the *Eagle*, *Edinburgh Castle* and *Hawk*, were converted into schooners.[36]

Davy's memoranda amplify the few facts that are already known about Peter Hedderwick. They tell us, for instance, that he also 'composed' six small galliots built in Robert Davy's yards for use on a canal in Scotland, presumably the Forth and Clyde. These 'very pritty' round-sterned vessels were known there as 'gabbarts', but in *Lloyd's Registers of Shipping* were mostly listed as luggers or as sloops. They had to be able to lower their masts for canal work.[37] Possibly Hedderwick was also connected with the sloop *Bee*, 53 tons, built by Robert Davy in 1815 for the Edinburgh, Glasgow and Leith Shipping Company, for she is mentioned more than once in the *Treatise*.

[31]Many of the Berwick smacks had artificial wells for carrying the salmon alive (Reid, op. cit., p. 15).

[32]Names of vessels from Reid's *Directory*; building places mostly obtained from *Lloyd's Register of Shipping* for 1820.

[33]Hedderwick's Leith smack with a redrawn sail plan is depicted by David R. MacGregor, *Merchant Sailing Ships 1815–1850*, Conway Maritime Press, 1984, p. 71.

[34]Hedderwick's *Treatise*, p. 102.

[35]Notice pasted into copy of Reid's *Directory*: 'These smacks are now replaced by the splendid steamers of the London and Edinburgh Shipping Company, sailing three times a week between Hermitage Wharf, London and Victoria Dock, Leith. First class fare 22/- in place of 73/6 by smack!'

[36]*Lloyd's Registers of Shipping*, 1838 and 1847.

[37]For illustrations of Forth and Clyde Canal gabbarts see Robert Simper, *Scottish Sail*, David and Charles, Newton Abbot, 1974, pp. 39–40.

Hedderwick gave Daniel Bishop Davy a plan of the breadths of vessels in general which the young Topsham shipbuilder started to note down in his Memoranda Book. However, after remarking that it answered well for good-proportioned vessels but hinting that he had a reservation about it, Davy left off and never completed the sentence, as will be seen in the transcript (text, p. 2). Hedderwick's *Treatise,* published 13 years afterwards, contains tables 'shewing the general proportion of length, breadth and depth of the different classes of merchant ships', and these provide the missing information. The tables were based on ten ships and vessels which Hedderwick considered to be of the best proportion of breadth to length, one of them being the smack *Regent,* 142 tons, tender to the Northern Lighthouses and built at Topsham to a plan drawn by D. B. Davy. 'This vessel,' observed Peter Hedderwick, 'stands well up to her canvas, and sails fast.' Table 1 is taken from the *Treatise.*

A Table of the Length, Breadth, and Depth of Schooners, Brigs, and Ships.

Length.	Breadth.		Depth.		Tonnage.	Length.	Breadth.		Depth.		Tonnage.	Length.	Breadth.		Depth.		Tonnage.
Feet.	Feet.	In.	Feet.	In.		Feet.	Feet.	In.	Feet.	In.		Feet.	Feet.	In.	Feet.	In.	
50	16	5	10	1½	57.54	86	25	1	16	10½	237.41	122	31	11½	22	3	558.58
52	16	11	10	6	63.66	88	25	6	17	3	251.42	124	32	4½	22	6	583.15
54	17	5	10	10½	70.25	90	25	11	17	7	265.93	126	32	9	22	9	606.69
56	17	11	11	3½	77.24	92	26	4	17	11	281.6	128	33	1½	23	0	631.14
58	18	5	11	8	84.66	94	26	9	18	3	296.65	130	33	6½	23	3	657.49
60	18	11	12	0	92.56	96	27	2	18	7	312.82	132	33	10½	23	6	681.60
62	19	5	12	4	100.91	98	27	6½	18	11	328.69	134	34	3½	23	9	709.43
64	19	11	12	9	109.77	100	27	11	19	3	345.10	136	34	8½	24	0	738.3
66	20	5	13	2	119.16	102	28	3½	19	7½	362.0	138	35	1	24	3½	765.64
68	20	11	13	6	129.3	104	28	8½	19	10½	380.38	140	35	5½	24	7½	793.87
70	21	5	13	11	139.40	106	29	1	20	1½	398.37	142	35	10½	24	10½	824.73
72	21	11	14	3½	150.34	108	29	5½	20	5	416.82	144	36	3½	25	2	856.29
74	22	5	14	8½	161.79	110	29	10	20	8	436.1	146	36	8½	25	5	888.59
76	22	10½	15	1	173.31	112	30	2½	20	11½	455.62	148	37	1½	25	8	921.70
78	23	4	15	5	185.32	114	30	6½	21	2	474.66	150	37	6½	25	11	954.82
80	23	9½	15	9½	197.83	116	30	11	21	5	495.43	152	38	0	26	2	992.35
82	24	3	16	1½	210.92	118	31	3½	21	8	510.11	154	38	6	26	5	1032.4
84	24	8	16	6	223.90	120	31	7½	21	11½	537.44	156	39	0	26	8	1072.74

Table 1. From *A Treatise on Marine Architecture* by Peter Hedderwick, Edinburgh 1830, p. 149. The figures after the points in the tonnage columns represent ninety-fourths: for example, 57.54 is $57^{54}/_{94}$ tons.

By way of comparison, Table 2 sets out the main proportions of schooners built or owned on the Exe during the period 1782 to 1869. This shows that the *Mary,* built by Robert Davy in 1816, was slightly narrower than Hedderwick's ideal and that many of those built later in the nineteenth century, among others by John Holman of Topsham, were markedly longer and proportionately narrower. As earlier noted, *Racer* and *Ace of Trumps,* built in the early 1830s by D. B. Davy, possibly for the Azores fruit trade – they had to race back with highly perishable cargoes – were sleeker vessels than, say, the *Swift,* which the Memoranda Book tells us was designed to trade between Exeter and London.

Costs and materials

The Memoranda Book provides a mass of information on timber and building costs, not only at Topsham but at Dartmouth, South Coast ports,

Greenock and Hull; it shows that the Davys contracted to build only the hull of a vessel and, unless specified, excluded the cabin, masts and spars, plumbing (i.e. leadwork) and painting. They charged so much 'per register ton'. The lowest price mentioned is £5 per ton for the lighters *Majestic* and *Neptune*. These were small vessels of shallow draught, but even so the price was too low and losses were incurred on both. Prices for schooners of less than a hundred tons in the period 1819 to 1824 ranged from £10 to £10 10s per ton. Daniel Davy estimated that in the case of a large, full-rigged ship of 430 tons, he could not charge less than £15 to £16 per ton 'to get anything by it'. Other builders, he tells us, were prepared to build ships complete and fit for sea, supplying everything 'even to a tinder box and spy glass' (text, p. 14).

Vessels from the Davy shipyards were, to borrow a phrase found in one of their own advertisements, 'strong and faithfully built' (text, p. 80). The frames were made entirely of oak timber, and oak planking was used both inside and out. The keels consisted of several large pieces of elm scarfed together. A quantity of elm plank was used about the bilges, and the decks were planked with fir, nailed down. Cylindrical oak treenails, tightened with wedges and punches (referred to as 'puncheons' in the manuscript), and iron or copper bolts were employed to fasten the hull together. The latter metal was the more expensive and added about five per cent per ton to the building costs. The vessels were invariably carvel built and the seams were filled with strands of oakum and payed with hot pitch. Shipbuilding timber was bought and sold by the load; a load was 50 feet, and this was supposed to weigh a ton (see *Timber* in Glossary). Various prices are recorded in the manuscript, ranging for oak from £6 per load to £8 15s per load for large Navy timber. Elm keel pieces were sold by the foot.

Analysis of expenditure on the London to Leith smack *Edinburgh Castle* (text, pp. 27–9) shows that materials were the major cost. She was built at Topsham in 1819 for a contract price of £2324 14s, i.e. 189 tons at £12 6s per ton. The oak timber cost the Davys £897 6s 3d; elm timber £33 2s 6d; oak plank £617 1s 0d; elm plank £36 0s 0d; fir plank £116 4s 10d; and joiners' deal £16 10s 10d: total £1716 5s 5d. In addition treenails cost £23 12s 6d; oakum £13 4s 0d; tar £1 8s 0d; pitch £1 18s 6d; wedges £3 13s 4d; rosin £1 10s 0d; iron nails £6 5s 0d; iron £120; and copper fastenings £232 3s 9d: total £403 15s 1d. Eleven hundredweight of oakum was used to caulk the seams, representing one hundredweight for every 17.2 tons. *Lloyd's Register of Shipping* for 1820 records that the *Edinburgh Castle* had iron standards and knees, hence the £120 bill for iron. Shipwrights' labour was charged at 30s per ton, £283 10s 0d; caulkers' labour at 3s per ton, £28 17s 0d; and joiners' labour at £24 2s 0d: total £336 9s 0d. The overall cost of the hull was £2456 9s 6d. Materials amounted to 86.3 per cent of the total and labour the remaining 13.7 per cent. The result was a loss to the shipbuilder of £131 15s 6d, an all too common occurrence at that time, as D. B. Davy found when he travelled around the coast (text, pp. 13–14).

Davy's manuscript makes it clear that prices were pared down to the bone with little, if any, allowance made for overheads, some of the builders, those at Hull, for example, relying on repairs for the bulk of their turnover. In the years 1818 and 1819 Daniel and his father, in addition to losing money on the *Edinburgh Castle*, lost heavily on the schooner *Three Sisters* and

Name	Builder	Where built	Year	Length in feet	Breadth in feet	Depth of hold in feet	Proportion of breadth to length	Comparison with Hedderwick's ideal (1830)
PEGGY of Exeter		Harbour Grace, Newfoundland	1782	46.0	13.3	6.8	3.46	Noticeably narrower
ENDEAVOUR of Exmouth	John Conant	Sidmouth	1788	55.0	16.3	8.1	3.37	Narrower
MARY of Exmouth	R. Davy	Topsham	1816	60.6	18.1	9.2	3.35	Slightly narrower
BRITANNIA of Exmouth	R. Davy	Topsham	1822	62.3	19.1	10.5	3.26	Slightly narrower
SWIFT of Exeter	R. Davy	Topsham	1824	62.5	19.0	10.0	3.29	Slightly narrower
POST BOY of Exeter	D. B. Davy	Topsham	1831	76.6	19.5	11.8	3.93	More than 3ft narrower
ACE OF TRUMPS of Exeter	D. B. Davy	Topsham	1833	60.5	16.5	9.7	3.67	2ft narrower
WILLIAM & CHARLES of Exeter	Walters & Wishart	Exmouth	1842	76.2	21.7	12.5	3.51	Slightly narrower
JUDY of Exeter	Holman & Walters	Topsham	1848	86.0	22.0	12.5	3.90	3ft narrower
COME ON of Exeter	J. Holman	Topsham	1854	106.0	20.2	11.0	5.25	About 9ft narrower
BLACK CAT of Teignmouth	J. B. Mansfield	Exeter	1857	88.7	20.0	11.8	4.44	5½ft narrower
ENGLAND'S ROSE of Topsham	J. Holman	Topsham	1858	104.0	21.0	11.5	4.95	7½ft narrower
JOHN WALTERS of Exeter	J. Walters	Exmouth	1866	97.0	21.4	12.4	4.53	markedly narrower
FLORENCE of Exeter	Holman & Sons	Topsham	1866	84.8	20.1	10.5	4.22	4½ft narrower
COQUETTE of Exeter	R. Redway	Exmouth	1869	99.4	21.2	11.5	4.69	6ft narrower

Table. 2. Comparison of the main proportions of Schooners, 1782–1869. Sources: Exeter Customs House records, *Lloyd's Registers of Shipping* and Exeter newspaper reports of launchings.

slightly on the sloop *Flower,* but managed to make a substantial profit on the *Regent,* built for £15 per ton, copper fastened to the wales. Some of the losses, however, were cushioned by the fact that, as already indicated, the builders often had a share in the vessels.

Four main categories of craftsmen were employed: shipwrights, caulkers, joiners and sawyers. Davy does not record wages but indicates that the work was contracted out to gangs who received so much per register ton of the vessels that they built. He states (text, p. 47) that the shipwright Thomas Bishop undertook to build the brig *Sedulous* in the Gulpit yard for 30s per ton. The same sum for shipwrights' labour is mentioned elsewhere in the Memoranda Book, although the rate fell to 25s per ton for small vessels such as lighters and rose to 35s per ton for the lighthouse tender *Regent* (text, p. 32), built to a superior specification. Caulkers' labour varied from 2s 6d per ton for a lighter to 4s 6d per ton for a full-rigged ship. A typical sum received by joiners was 5s per ton. Sawyers working on the sloop *Fortitude* and other vessels received 3s per hundred foot of sawn timber. The cost of launching varied from £5 to £20, depending on the size of vessel.

The Holman collection at the Topsham Museum includes the original contract, dated 7 November 1827, for the schooner *Ebenezer,* built by Daniel Bishop Davy at the Passage yard, Topsham, for Captain John Holman and others. Davy himself owned a one-eighth part of the vessel. The document states that she was to be built of 'good English oak except where it is specifically mention'd to be otherwise'; the bilge strakes were to be of 'good elmn' and those parts of the deck which were not of oak were to be 'of the best Dantzic or Norway timber, six inches wide, 2½ ins thick', and the bulwarks of 'best red deal'. The shipbuilder agreed 'to fix a figurehead with rails &c complete', the owners finding the figure, and 'to fit up a neat mahogany cabin and sufficient bed cabins in the forcastle (*sic*)'. He also agreed to supply two ship's boats. The contract price was £11 10s per ton, the money to be paid in three instalments: 'one-third when the keel, floors, stem and stern are up and one-third when the timbers are in and the bends work'd and one-third when the said vessell is complete and del[ivere]d in safety'. She had 'to be completed and launch'd on or before the 20th June 1828', and a penalty for 'non performance' of the agreement was set at £150. The document is particularly detailed about the sizes of the timbers and the way the vessel was to be fastened together; it is printed in full as Appendix D.

Ships for the Royal Navy

Daniel Davy lists the different Royal Navy ships built by his father during the Napoleonic Wars (text, p. 58). Some were launched at Gulpit, Countess Wear, and others at Topsham. He gives the names of sixteen and also mentions an unnamed sailing lighter – the *Falmouth,* possibly – and two mooring lighters. Two other Topsham builders, Obadiah Ayles and Thomas Owen, each built five men-of-war during this period, and a third contractor, John Bass, built one at Lympstone, the gun-brig *Urgent,* and one at Topsham, the *Cyane,* a 540-ton, 22-gun sixth rate which had the misfortune to be captured in 1815 by the U.S.S. *Constitution* in the

Atlantic;[38] but both Ayles[39] and Owen[40] went bankrupt and the only builder launching warships on the Exe from 1808 onwards was Robert Davy.

Although the term 'H.M.S.' was coming into use gradually, being first used towards the end of the eighteenth century,[41] it is not found in this manuscript nor in contemporary newspaper reports referring to vessels built on the Exe. Normally, Plymouth Dockyard was the only place in Devon where Royal Navy ships were built, but with the renewal of war with France in 1803 contracts were also awarded to merchant shipyards to meet the Admiralty's exceptional demands for new tonnage. Two large 74-gun ships were built at Turnchapel, near Plymouth, and Dartmouth and Bideford each contributed about 15 smaller vessels; but as Table 3 shows, none of these places could match Topsham, which launched no fewer than 28 sixth-rates, sloops-of-war, bomb-ketches and gun-brigs.

Comparisons between launching dates and sailing reports show that the vessels built on the Exe remained on the river for several weeks. One of them, the *Weazle,* built at Topsham by Thomas Owen, was copper bottomed at Exmouth (text, p. 78). Newspaper reports of the time record the arrival of dockyard lighters and transports with riggers and stores and the new warships were then given a 'jury' or temporary rigging and escorted down the coast to Plymouth Dock (now Devonport) by a Royal Navy cutter or gun-brig. The need for ships at that time was such that they usually 'went up the harbour directly to be fitted for sea'. Some of the later ones, all built by Robert Davy, were fitted out at Portsmouth, including the gun-brigs *Adder* and *Clinker* and the bomb-ketch *Terror,* which sailed from Exmouth together under the escort of the *Gambier* cutter about the beginning of August 1813 (text, p. 79).

In later years the *Terror* was to become famous as a polar exploration vessel, both in the Arctic and the Antarctic, but she was a rather odd-looking vessel when first fitted out. She and her Davy-built sister ship, the appropriately named *Vesuvius*, each had two mortars with which to hurl high explosive bombs at a steep angle at shore positions. They also carried other guns and in appearance resembled a three-masted ship minus its foremast. The mortars were mounted in the space between the bowsprit and the mainmast, the forestays of the latter being made of iron chain to withstand the upward flash during firing. They were very strongly built.[42] The *Terror* took part in the bombardment of Baltimore in 1814, served later in the Mediterranean and, after nearly a decade as a discovery vessel, was fitted in 1845 with auxiliary steam power for Sir John Franklin's tragic

[38]J.J.Colledge, *Ships of the Royal Navy,* an historical index, Vol. 1, Major ships, David and Charles, Newton Abbot, 1969.

[39]Obadiah Ayles of Topsham, shipbuilder, bankrupt, *Trewman's Exeter Flying-Post,* 2 July 1807.

[40]'To be sold, by order of the assignees of Thomas Owen, a bankrupt . . . all that dwelling-house, and shipwright's yard called Sandford's Quay, situate on the Strand, adjoining the river Exe, in the town of Topsham, and now in the occupation of Mr Thomas Owen, the younger, shipbuilder . . . Also, a slip, on and from which vessels of about 400 tons may be built and launched . . .' (*Woolmer's Exeter and Plymouth Gazette,* 18 June 1814).

[41]Introduction to E.H.H. Archibald, *Ship Portraits in the National Maritime Museum,* H.M.S.O., London, reprinted 1962.

[42]James Henderson, *Sloops and Brigs,* Adlard Coles Ltd, London, 1972, p. 19.

expedition in search of the North-West Passage, from which no one returned. The *Terror* and her companion vessel, the Pembroke-built *Erebus*, after being beset in the ice, were finally abandoned on 22 April 1848.[43] Following the final defeat of Napoleon in 1815 some of the Topsham ships were sold out of the Navy and several became East Indiamen or South Seas whalers. Two of Davy's ships, *Clinker* and *Pelican*, were still afloat in the 1860s as coastguard watch vessels.[44]

Topsham		Bideford		Dartmouth	
1804	Piercer	1806	Mutine	1804	Staunch
	Rapid (i)	1807	Garland		Wolf
	Swinger		Volage	1805	Brisk
	Safeguard		Comet		Martin
1805	Surinam		Myrtle		Star
	Weazle		Carnation		Swallow
	Wolverine	1812	Fairy		Turbulent
	Adder (i)	1813	Ontario		Virago
	Bustler		Mastiff	1806	Thais
	Conflict		Beelzebub		Ferret
1806	Daphne		Pelter	1809	Hesper
	Lightning	1814	Falmouth		Partridge
	Tartarus		Cyrene	1810	North Star
	Cyane	1817	Tees	1813	Dartmouth
1807	Porcupine				Erne
	Erebus				
	Fawn	**Fremington**			
	Falmouth			**Ringmore**	
1808	Rapid (ii)	1806	Delight		
1809	Scylla	1807	Ranger	1805	Wizard
1812	Wasp			1806	Anacreon
	Pelican	**Turnchapel**			Rook
1813	Clinker				Landrail
	Terror	1807	Derwent	1812	Perseus
	Vesuvius	1810	Armada		
	Adder (ii)	1812	Clarence		
1814	Hind				
	Tyne	**Teignmouth**			
——	Mooring lighters	1807	Talbot		

Lympstone		**Brixham**	
1804	Urgent	1806	Widgeon
			Sealark

Table 3. Warships built in Devonshire merchant yards 1804–17. Sources: Davy's Memoranda Book, contemporary newspapers, J. J. Colledge, *Ships of the Royal Navy, an historical index*, Vol. 1, David & Charles, 1969, Grahame Farr, *Shipbuilding in North Devon*, National Maritime Museum, Greenwich, 1976 and M. M. Oppenheim, *The Maritime History of Devon*, University of Exeter, 1968.

[43]J. Douglas Hoare, *Arctic Exploration*, Methuen, 1906, pp. 174–5.
[44]Colledge, op. cit.

LARGE MERCHANTMEN

At the beginning of the nineteenth century the main shipbuilders on the Exe, besides Robert Davy, were John Bass at Lympstone and Obadiah Ayles, Thomas Owen and Tilney Rising at Topsham. In 1804 Captain Rising's yard at the lower end of Topsham Strand[45] was acquired by John Bishop who was briefly in partnership there with Bass.[46] The merchant ships constructed at this period included some of the largest ever built on the river. Among them were the East Indiamen: *Retreat*, 505 tons, built by Ayles in 1801,[47] and the *Glory*, 538 tons.[48] But biggest of all was Davy's 600-ton *Caroline*, launched at Countess Wear in 1802 and subsequently renamed *Batavia*. She drew 20 ft when loaded and, as Francis Davy tells us, there were immense problems in getting such large ships down the shallow river above Topsham. Sometimes they were floated on casks and 'lifted also by barges fastened down to them by chains'. Exmouth Bar was an additional hazard and it was said that vessels of heavy tonnage were similarly 'cameled' over it.[49] The *Batavia* was chartered by the East India Company and on one of her voyages sailed from London on 9 June 1810, bound for Madras and Bengal under the command of Captain J. Mayne. For protection she carried two 12-pounder guns and ten 18-pounder short guns 'on the new construction'. She was not listed in 1820. Another Davy ship, the *Earl St Vincent*, 423 tons and built in 1800 to trade to Jamaica, was later switched to the East India service and made voyages to Bombay and Java.[50]

During a lull in his warship work in 1810 and 1811, Robert Davy built three full-rigged merchant ships, *Phoenix*, *Jamaica Planter* and *Medina*. Although she was built before he began, Daniel Davy was familiar with the plan ('draft' No 5) of the *Jamaica Planter*. 'She answered extremely well & was a very beautiful ship', he states. Sadly, she was lost with all hands on her second homeward passage from Jamaica. A correspondent, Mr Martin Benn, has obtained from shipping records the following details of her short career.

> Captain James Smith: 13 March 1811 sailed Portsmouth in a convoy for Jamaica; 5 April arrived Madeira; 12 May arrived Jamaica; 20 August sailed Jamaica; 19 October arrived in the Thames.
> Captain Hutton: 19 February 1812 sailed Thames for Jamaica; 10 March sailed Portsmouth in a convoy for Jamaica; 10 May arrived Jamaica; 31 July sailed Jamaica in a convoy for London; 27 August with the *Lord Cochrane*, became separated from the fleet during a heavy gale in the latitude of Bermuda and both ships went missing.

[45]Tilney Rising's shipyard advertised for sale, *Trewman's Exeter Flying-Post*, 18 August 1803. Also mentioned in Devon Record Office, Volume of transcripts of Topsham deeds in the possession of Hugh Wilson Holman et al., Nos. 599–605.

[46]Partnership dissolved by mutual consent, *Trewman's Exeter Flying-Post*, 11 December 1806.

[47]*Lloyd's Register of Shipping* for 1812 describes her as an 'extra ship' in the East India Company's service, taken up for four voyages. A letter to the company concerning her is reprinted by David R. MacGregor, *Merchant Sailing Ships, 1775–1815*, p. 26.

[48]Listed on a voyage from London to India, *Lloyd's Register of Shipping* for 1812.

[49]Report of the opening of the Strand graving dock, Topsham, supplement to *The Western Times*, 5 June 1858.

[50]*Lloyd's Registers of Shipping*, 1820 and 1828.

The loss of the *Jamaica Planter* is referred to in the Biography of Robert Davy in which it is stated that she was fitted out at Topsham at a cost of £18,000. According to *Lloyd's Register* for 1812 she carried twenty guns. She was first registered at Exeter on 15 December 1810 and just over a year later was registered anew in London. A one-eighth part of her was sold in November 1811 for £1,800. Robert Davy himself was a part-owner.[51]

The Indiaman *Medina* is depicted in a fine oil painting by Thomas Whitcombe (Plate 4), formerly in the Science Museum, London. She was built at Topsham in 1811 and when registered at Exeter on 25 July that year was described as having three masts, two decks and a woman figurehead. Her extreme length aloft was 121 ft 8 in., extreme breadth 29 ft 5¾ in. and height between decks 6 ft 8½in. She was a square-sterned ship with two quarter galleries and was 469¹⁷⁄₉₄ tons burden. Her original owners included Robert Davy, her captain, John Kennedy of London, and Charles, George, Robert and Edmund Francis Green, all of the city of London. Her Exeter registration was cancelled in October 1812 and she was registered anew in London.[52] Daniel Davy informs us (text, p. 61) that his father still owned a one-eighth part of her in 1822. In Whitcombe's painting the *Medina*, under London registration, is shown near Portsmouth, in three different positions, gradually increasing sail.

'STONE BOATS' AND LIME-BURNING

Lime-burning was formerly one of the principal industries of the Exe estuary. Old maps show kilns dotted along the shoreline and the remains of some of these ruggedly-built structures, including those operated by the Davys at Higher Wear and Lympstone, can still be seen. The vessels that served them were known as 'stone boats', and much of the stone came from coastal quarries at Babbacombe, Torquay. The Rev. John Swete, describing a visit there in 1793, noted:

A number of fishing smacks were just come to their moorings: and by the side of a projecting point of rock that lay nearly in the centre of the little bay, was a barge from Topsham receiving her cargo of limestone: to this spot do all these boats come [from the Exe].[53]

The design of the river Exe stone boats seems to have become standardised by the mid-eighteenth century. In the Exeter Customs House shipping registers they were invariably described as square-sterned sloops with part of a deck and one mast; they ranged from about 55 to 75 tons and were frequently about 54 feet long. Because the approaches to most of the kilns on the tidal stretches of the river were shallow, it was customary for the stone boats to unload their cargoes into lighters for the last part of the voyage. As the list made in 1822 of Robert Davy's shipping property shows (text, p. 61), each stone boat usually worked with two lighters, the *Lucy*, for example, having two such vessels belonging to her called *Increase* and *Tiger*. These were part-decked with one mast and a lugsail and were just over 40 ft

[51]Devon Record Office, Exeter Customs House, Register of Shipping, Vol. 1 (1786–1811), 1810, No. 39.
[52]Ibid. 1811, No. 23.
[53]Devon Record Office, 'Picturesque Sketches of Devon', vol. 6, p. 36.

long, about 15 ft 9 in. broad and just over 2½ ft deep in the hold. The *Increase* was square sterned but another Davy-owned lighter, the *Greyhound*, was round-sterned.[54] Sometimes even the lighters were unable to approach the kilns and the stones were then thrown overboard in heaps, to be carried ashore when the tide went out.[55] In 1827 Robert Davy stated in a navigation dispute that his 'boats and barges' going upriver passed a place called the Broad, above Topsham, 'about half-tide in order to enable them to get up to Wear with the power of the tide & unload & return down again with the ebbing of the same tide'.[56]

Daniel Davy gives details of the *Eclipse* stone boat, 76²⁰/₉₄ tons, built in 1819 at Gulpit 'to carry stones from Torbay to Topsham'. The shipwright in charge of her construction was Thomas Bishop and she was built entirely of oak, with deal plank used for the rudder case, wedges for the mast, deck, hatches and bulwarks. She was fastened with treenails and iron bolts. The actual cost of the hull was £768 14s 9d, a figure representing just over £10 a ton. She was a successful vessel and 'sailed very fair'; but the same could not be said of the *Ceres*, an 85-ton stone boat built in Robert Davy's Passage yard at Topsham the previous year. She was designed by Thomas Bowden and in D. B. Davy's opinion was not a very good model. He lists several faults and states 'she drew one foot too much for the stone trade and was too large altogether for her use'. The *Ceres* was then lengthened and rebuilt as a schooner and under the Davys' ownership traded for many years, making voyages to the Tyne and to Ireland, before being sold to Cornish owners.[57] Interestingly, D. B. Davy noted (text, p. 4) that she was the first Exe stone boat to have a chain anchor cable instead of a hempen one, and she also had a patent winch for raising her mainsail.

D. B. Davy states in his memoranda that his father's stone boats carried 45 tons and each load when burnt made on average 67½ hogsheads of lime. In 1822 the family's kilns at four separate locations – Wear, Gulpit, Marsh and Lympstone – produced 37,305 hogsheads, a figure which represents 552 voyages by the stone boats or, assuming each one discharged into two lighters, 1104 bargeloads. The scale of this business was indeed considerable. The Lympstone kilns 'where the lime trade has been carried on for many years past by Mr. Davy' were advertised to let in December 1835, with the offer that 'the stone boat and lighters which supply the said kilns may be taken at a valuation'. These kilns now form a wall at the water's edge near the clock tower. Another set which the Davys were operating in 1850 were the Maer kilns at Exmouth.[58]

A contract for a stone boat built at Topsham in 1802 by Thomas Owen is printed as Appendix C. This vessel was equipped with a mainsail, foresail,

[54]Devon Record Office, Exeter Customs House, Register of Shipping, Vol. 4 (1825–29), entries dated 30 December 1826.

[55]E. A. G. Clark, *The Ports of the Exe Estuary*, University of Exeter, reprinted 1962, p. 82. An old postcard shows stone heaped in the river near the Davy kilns at Higher Wear (Plate 9); they remained in use until about 1914, Bartlett, 'A Manuscript History of Countess Wear', Westcountry Studies Library, Exeter.

[56]Devon Record Office, Attorney General & Exeter v Davy, loc. cit., note 9.

[57]*Lloyd's Registers of Shipping*, 1820–62: her Exeter registration was cancelled and she was registered anew at Truro on 22 June 1848 (Devon Record Office: Exeter Customs House Register of Shipping, Vol. 5, note added to entry No. 39, 27 May 1836).

[58] White's *Directory*, p. 230.

two jibs and a squaresail. Similar single-masted sloops were employed in the trade between Exeter and London, but they were usually longer and deeper in the hold. The *Fortitude* was among those built by the Davys, but in 1824 she was one of three regular 'London traders' to be re-rigged as a two-masted schooner.[59]

Like his father, Daniel Bishop Davy was clearly a shrewd businessman and his painstaking efforts to set down how much ships actually cost to build and his similar exercises to find out how much it cost to burn a hogshead of lime or for an anchorsmith to make 35 fathom of ⅝ inch chain cable for a stone boat, are remarkable, the last-mentioned being especially so because it clearly demonstrated to him that chainmaking could be a profitable business. Anchors and chain cables manufactured by D. B. Davy were prominent in the 1820s and 1830s in Topsham's important export trade of marine stores to ports on the English southern coast.[60]

THOMAS BOWDEN

The name of Thomas Bowden, designer of the *Ceres,* is linked in the manuscript through his initials 'T.B.' with four other Davy vessels: the brig *Mary,* the schooners *Perseverance* and *Three Sisters* and an unnamed yacht (text, pp. 59–60). In the Topsham parish registers he was described as a shipwright when he married Frances Hannaford on 10 September 1818 and, later, when one of their sons was baptised, as a master shipwright. Finally, he was described as a shipbuilder. In 1824 Bowden became Daniel Davy's main rival in the town when he took over the Strand End shipyard;[61] he launched, among others, the schooners *Thames,*[62] *City of Exeter*[63] and *Peamore.*[64] In 1844 he lengthened the schooner yacht *Janette,* built at Shoreham, Sussex, in 1826 and owned by the Rt Honourable George Wyndham, Earl of Egremont, of Silverton Park, Devon.[65] Bowden had earlier failed to repay an £800 mortgage and in November 1840 had been adjudged bankrupt.[66] Daniel Davy bought his shipyard at auction for £1,300 – more than enough to pay off the mortgage trustees.[67] Possibly Bowden resumed there as tenant, or nearby; but in April 1852 Davy let the yard to William, John and James Row, who subsequently built several ketches there. The 1851 Census records Thomas Bowden and his wife as aged 64 and 60 respectively and living in a house on the Strand, Topsham.

---

[59]Devon Record Office: Exeter Customs House Register of Shipping, Vol. 3 (1824–5), 1824, Nos. 4 and 74: the other vessels were the *Union* (Ibid. Nos. 11 and 100) and the *Commodore* (Ibid. Nos. 67 and 90).

[60]Clark, op. cit, p. 128.

[61]Devon Record Office, Transcripts of Topsham deeds, loc. cit., note 45, Nos 611–13.

[62]Report of her launching, *Trewman's Exeter Flying-Post,* 15 June 1826.

[63]Ibid. 29 July 1830.

[64]Ibid. 3 October 1839.

[65]Devon Record Office, Exeter Customs House, Register of Shipping, Vol. 6 (1838–47), 1844, No. 13: also *Trewman's Exeter Flying-Post,* 25 July 1844.

[66]Devon Record Office, Transcripts of Topsham deeds, 617.

[67]Devon Record Office, Typescript Precis of deeds, etc. relating to Topsham, No. DD49366, p. 147, yard described as 'late in the possession of Thomas Bowden'.

NOTES ON EDITING

The text is given in full and in the form in which it is laid out in Davy's volume. Every effort has been made to retain the style and flavour of the period, so as to present a nineteenth century original rather than a polished twentieth century edition; for this, after all, is not a book of sermons but a record of a hard and risky trade pursued by men with a greater knowledge of timber than of penmanship. Such alterations as have been made have been confined solely to the order of pages. The text now begins with names of ships and Davy's comments on them, followed, in some instances, by their basic dimensions. Inevitably this results in repetition, but is thought to be preferable to describing a vessel and then giving its dimensions at the opposite end of the text, which is the case in the manuscript. Lists giving the materials and costs of individual vessels have been grouped together in chronological sequence, as have detailed dimensions relating to plans ('drafts') of the sloop *Bee*, brigs *Sedulous*, *Mary* and *Dorothea* and schooners *Swift* and *Eliza*. The volume contains a number of loose papers and the more important of these have been inserted into the text where appropriate.

Davy's spelling has been followed throughout, but much of the punctuation is editorial. Names of ships have been put in italics, capitalisation has been modernised and superscript letters have been lowered. Abbreviations such as 'do' for 'ditto', 'pr' for 'per' and those for the months of the year have been extended, but '&' for 'and', '&c' for 'etc.' and christian names have been left in the form in which they appear: where Davy writes Jno for John, Thos for Thomas or Danl for his own name, they have not been changed. Prices are given in pounds, shillings and pence (£ s d) as in the text, but if the shipbuilder writes, say, 2/6 instead of 2s 6d, the latter form has been substituted. The symbol @ has been altered to 'at'. Square brackets are used to indicate blanks in the text and to enclose editorial insertions. They are also used with a question mark in cases where the transcription cannot be guaranteed. For the sake of completeness, the occasional puzzling passage has been included, if necessary without explanation; this is also the case with some of the quantities mentioned, and the sharp-eyed will detect discrepancies here and there in Davy's casting of his formidable lists of figures. The text is given without reference to the pagination of the original, this being somewhat idiosyncratic; but the occurrence of such phrases as 'carried over' and 'brought up' indicate where some of the pages end and begin in the manuscript.

TOPSHAM JUBILEE

Exactly 50 years ago, in 1938, the Devon and Cornwall Record Society published the parish registers of Topsham, transcribed and edited by H. Tapley-Soper and dedicated to the memory of Hugh Wilson Holman, whose private house called Furlong and its garden occupied the site of the Passage shipyard, from which the Davys launched both warships and merchantmen. The registers record the life cycles of many of the town's former shipbuilders and shipwrights and reveal the multifarious occupations of the people who once formed its maritime community: the sail, rope, stay and block makers, the chain, cable and anchor smiths, the joiners, carpenters and caulkers, timber-hewers, sawyers, chandlers, mariners, lightermen, tide-waiters and pilots. This volume shows that community at work, ably led by such men as Daniel Davy. As will have been gathered already, his memoranda give a rare and individual account of shipbuilding in the age of oak; they also provide a glimpse of a vanished era when lime-burning and other industries flourished in small, out of the way places such as Countess Wear. Horses and carts once thronged the lanes around the estuary kilns and working boats paraded daily up and down the tidal Exe, bringing groceries and ironmongery for the shops, coal, stone and many of the other cargoes that now go by rail and road. But most remarkable was the scale of the shipbuilding: a 600-ton East Indiaman rising above the reedbeds in the shipyard at Glasshouse must have been an unforgettable sight, like the *Queen Mary* towering over Clydeside. Clearly, Davy's volume offers scope for further analysis and comment, tasks for those contributing to the University of Exeter's 'New Maritime History of Devon'. The main object here has been to provide an accurate text.

ACKNOWLEDGEMENTS

The editor and the Council of the Devon & Cornwall Record Society wish to thank Exeter City Council and the Topsham Museum Society for permission to publish these records. They are also greatly indebted to the Topsham Market House Trust and Devon estate agents Fulfords for generous donations which have enabled illustrations to be included.

The editor is particularly grateful to Mrs Barbara Entwistle, chairman of the Topsham Museum Society, for her help in various ways, including depositing temporarily in the Devon Record Office the various Davy documents, and to Professor Joyce Youings for much invaluable advice and for preparing this volume for publication. Dr David Starkey of the University of Exeter's Maritime History of Devon Project read through the Introduction and suggested various improvements which were subsequently incorporated, and Mr Robin Imray of London placed at the editor's disposal his researches on the *Post Boy, Racer, Ace of Trumps* and other vessels built by D. B. Davy. Once again, the Devon county archivist Mrs Margery Rowe and her staff gave every assistance. The extracts from Exeter newspapers were made from copies in the Westcountry Studies Library, Exeter, and the Devon and Exeter Institution Library in the Cathedral Close, Exeter.

Among individuals who should be thanked are the following: Mr Arthur Credland, keeper of maritime history at the Town Docks Museum, Hull; Mr David White, curator, Draught Room, National Maritime Museum, Greenwich; Dr H. Tomlinson, chief librarian, the Priaulx Library, Guernsey; Mr Roy Wheeler, Mr Francis Luscombe, Mr Gerald Walker, Mr John Leyman and Mr Roy Rundle.

Bath,
April 1988

Clive N. Ponsford

DANIEL BISHOP DAVY'S MEMORANDA BOOK

[Front cover with a large letter A]

Dimensions of Ships
- Laid down 1817 -
Sundry memorandoms on
Ship Building, Lime burning
Timber trade &c &c

[Title page]   Danl B Davy 1817

Dimensions of different ships laid down by Davy with his remarks & memorandums

[There is a brief guide to the contents, containing just two entries: a reference to the lists of 'different ships built by Robert Davy both Navy & merchant' and another to the writer's 'remarks on different subjects concerning ships & building', the latter being the section of the manuscript beginning with an account of his visit to Greenock. The inside back cover is also inscribed with the date 1817 and has a small, oval-shaped pink label, indicating that originally the book had been 'Sold by W. Curson, Library, Exeter'.]

NAMES OF SHIPS WITH REMARKS ON THEM & BY WHOM COMPOSED, 1817 [–1827]

1817
No 1   Sloop call'd *Heroine* of 111^{18}/94 ton [s] but not built at Topsham. Too circular a body – would roll in a sea *very much* – but good proportions, only rather too sharp; sailes very fast. Should not like to compose by her but if did would make her carry her flatness much further aft.

1817
No 2   Sloop call'd *Partunda* (a Brixham trawl-boat) of 37^{49}/94 ton[s] which answer'd very well & sailed remarkably fast. A good draft to compose such a vessel by.

1817
No 3   Brig call'd *Tutoress* of 211^{25}/94 ton [s] composed by D. B. Davy – her stern too heavy. Main bread[t]h not quite high enough – say 2 ft or 2½ ft higher would make her looks better; & her flatness carried further aft would make her a good looking vessel & carry a large cargo & sail well & stand without bal[l]ast.

1

1817

No 4   Brig call'd *Sally* of 282²¹⁄94 [tons] composed by Danl B. Davy. Main breadth not quite high enough (say 2½ ft higher), too full at the harpin, & stern if any thing rather heavy, but good in a sea. Should like to build by her if I had occasion to build about her size & to lean aft if any thing. Refer to Mr Hed[d]erwick's proportions as to the steerage frame & breadth as to his plan which he gave me, as [it] is a very good one in general.

1817

No 5   Ship call'd *Jamaica Planter* of 424⁵⁸⁄94 [tons], built by Robt Davy before I begune, but answered extremely well & was a very beautiful ship. Should like – if had occasion – to build by her or compose if I had a vessel to build about her size. Is now lost with all hands, suppos'd to have foundered at sea or upset by shifting, her cargo not being properly shipp'd.

[The Exeter Customs House Register of Shipping (Vol. 1 1786–1811) records that she was built at Topsham in 1810 and was 455³⁸⁄94 tons 'burthen'. She was first registered on 15 December that year (No. 39). See Introduction, pp. xxiv–xxv and Biography of Robert Davy.]

1817

No 6   Brig – name unknown – of 177²⁷⁄94 [tons], built by Robt Davy, composed by (*I believe*) Mr Thankful Sturdee (my remarks). Main breadth not quite high enough. I would rise top breadth something, & floor sirmark a little on middle line but keep it the same on base line. If I had occasion would compose by it.

[Henry Parker Sturdee, son of Thankful and Mary, was baptised at Topsham on 31 October 1808 and a daughter, Matilda Mary, was also baptised there, on 31 May 1810 (Topsham parish register). The British Museum General Catalogue of Books lists a Thankfull Sturdee as author of *Reminiscences of Old Deptford* (H. Richardson, London 1895). Royal Navy ships were built there. Davy's reference to 'my remarks' is puzzling, as this is the only time he mentions Mr Sturdee.]

1817

No 7   Six small vessels built for the Edinburgh, Glasgow & Leith Company, built by Robt Davy & composed by Mr P. Hed [d]erwick. Very pritty vessels, only round sterns and about 11 or 12 inches too narrow; if altered and made square sterns with 11 or 12 inches more breadth would be very fine vessels. If I had occasion to build any about their size would certainly build by them with the foresaid alterations. Names: *Fly, Star, Alert, Lark, Active & Dove.* All *answered well* (use, for traversing a canal in Scotland). Ton[n]age about 48 to 49 tons; if altered, more.

1817

No 8   A plan for the breadths of vessels in general which answers very well for good proportioned vessels given me by Mr Haderwick [Hedderwick] but I should

[Tantalisingly, the sentence finishes abruptly as above and no further details are given. Mr Peter Hedderwick was author of *A Treatise on Marine Architecture*, 1830. See Introduction pp. xvi–xviii.]

1818

No 9   A brig call'd the *Sedulous* composed by myself of about 134 tons, built at [Countess] Wear. About six inches too high & rather to [o] full forward but more especially aft, the frames from 10 to 16 ought to be six inches of a side cleaner from F S [floor sirmark] to 1 S [first foothook sirmark]; and likewise forward a little with the stem to have more rake. She was sold to Messrs Whitaway [Whiteway] & Mudge of Torquay who liked her very well for a vessel seeking general cargos. She carried from Treingmouth [Teignmouth] to Liverpoole the first voyage 193 tons of pipe clays, 2 tons of potatoes, 2 tons of oil, besides ship stores of different kinds, making in the whole about, I should suppose (allowing 2½ cwt more upon a ton of clay then 20 cwt to a ton) 225 tons regular weight, then drawing [   ] aft & [   ] aft.

Scantling of her frame

Sided		Moulded	
Floors	[-]	Floors	[-]
1 foothooks	[-]	1 foothooks	[-]
2 foothooks	[-]	2 foothooks	[-]
3 foothooks	[-]	3 foothooks	[-]
Top timbers	[-]	Top timbers	[-]
Beams upper	[-]	Upper beams	[-]
Lower beams	[-]	Lower beams	[-]
		Knees sided	[-]
		Hooks ditto	[-]

[See pp. 47–51 for detailed dimensions of this vessel. When the *Sedulous* was re-registered at Exeter on 7 March 1825 'Joseph Whiteway, merchant, of the parish of St. Nicholas [Shaldon]' was recorded as owning 32 of her 64 shares; her captain, Nicholas Mudge, mariner, of 'Tormoham' [Torquay], owned 16 (Exeter Customs House Register of Shipping, Vol. 3 1824–1825, No. 14 – 1825.) *Sedulous*: Diligent, active, constant in application to the matter in hand, persistent (*Shorter Oxford English Dictionary*).]

1818

No 10   A brig call'd the *Mary* composed by myself of 214 tons, built at Topsham. She was as good a model as can be built for a merchant man to sail well & carry a good cargo. She had a bust-head & carved stern with a neat quarter badge of 3 sham windows. The cabin was rather too small. She looked extremely well & had a very good sheer; in fact, I think nothing could be altered for the better. She had seven pair of iron standards on the hold beams besides the wood hanging & lodging knees; she had two pointer & a crutch aft. She was sold to Mr Peter Maze, merchant, Bristol, for the Mediterranean trade.

Scantling of her frame

Sided		Moulded	
Floors	11½ to 12 in.	Floors	mid[ship]s 12 in., head 9 in.
1 foothooks	10 to 10½ in.	1 foothooks	head 8 in.
2 ditto	9 in.	2 ditto	6½ [in.]
3 ditto	at heel 9, head 7 in.	3 ditto	5½ [in.]
Top timbers	7 in.	Top timbers	4¾ in.
Upper beams	11 in.	Upper beams	10 in.
Lower ditto	12 in.	Lower beams	10¼ in.
		Knees sided	6 in.
		Hooks ditto	9 in.

[Dimensions of] No 10

	Feet	inches
Length from the fore part of the main stem to the after part of stern post	82	6
Breadth extreme	24	0
Depth in the hold from skin to skin	15	10
Length on deck	87	6
Height of wing transom	14	0
Ditto of lower wales in midships	10	6
Room & space	1	11

Ton[n]age about 214 tons

[The late Grahame Farr in his *Records of Bristol Ships 1800-1838*, Bristol Record Society, 1950, lists the *Mary*, built at Topsham in 1818. She was variously rigged as a brig or as a snow. Farr describes her as a general trader which can be traced sailing to the Black Sea, Baltic and West Indies. She dropped out of *Lloyd's Register of Shipping* between 1841 and 1843.]

1818

No 11   A schooner [called the *Venus*] composed by myself of 83 tons, built at [Countess] Wear. She was a very good model & would require no alterations except in the luff of the bow which should be thrown out ab[o]ut 4 inches of a side, and if she was about 4in. wider altogether she would be better. She was sold to Mr Furneaux of Brixham who liked her extremely well & if I wanted to build about her size should certainly build from her draft.

[Omitted: 'Scantlings of her frame', the list like that of No. 9 not giving any details. The list of her main dimensions is similarly incomplete, except that it gives her tonnage as above, and this too has been omitted.]

1818

No 12   A stone [boat] called the *Ceres*, built at Topsham, of 85 tons. Was not a very good model being unfare [unfair] & rather to[o] full forward & aft. The most fault was in the second futtocks aft which had to[o] much buttock. She drew 1 foot too much water for the stone trade & was too large altogether for her use; her wales were tapered away to the thickness of the bottom below but the upper part had a projection as usual. She had a chain cable, the first any of the stone boats had, and likewise a patent wrinch [winch] in order to get up her main sail with greater ease. She was composed by Thomas Bowden.

Scantling of her frame [-]

[Dimensions of] No 12

	[Feet]	[inches]
Length from the fore part of main stem to the after part of stern post is	59	0
Length aloft on deck	61	
Breadth extreme	18	5½
Depth in hold to the deck	[-]	[-]
Depth to the plank share [sheer] in midships	[-]	[-]

Burthen in tons 85

Called the *Ceres* – the Goddess of Harvest

1818

No 13   A yacht built at Topsham called the [blank] for Captn Nesbitt R.N.
of Exmouth, composed by myself. She was a foot to[o] narrow & a foot to[o]
low to have any accommodations. She was a very good model but very
sharp. She had an alteration from the drawing which was a quarter deck aft
18 inches higher then [than] the other part of the deck & 8 feet long from the
fore part of the stern post.

[Dimensions of] No 13

	[Feet]	[inches]
Length from the fore part of main stem to the after part of stern post is	3[-]	[-]
Length aloft on deck	3[-]	[-]
Breadth extreme	10	[-]
Depth in hold	6	[-]
Burthen in tons 17^{90}/$_{94}$		
Called the [blank]		

1818

No 14   A schooner built at Topsham of 85 tons called the *Perseverance,* built
for Mr Hooper of Gatcombe of exactly the same form as No 11 [the *Venus*]
with no alteration whatever. Was liked extremely well & sail'd fast &
carried a very fair cargo. Should build all of her size by the same draft.
Scantling of her frame [-]

[Dimensions of] No 14

Length between the perpendiculars	[-]
Length aloft on deck	[-]
Breadth extreme	[-]
Depth in the hold	[-]
Burthen in tons 86 [1]	
Call'd *Perseverance*	
Captn Jno Hooper – Gatcombe nr Colyton	

[[1]The figure has been corrected by Davy from 85 to 86. The *Perseverance* was still afloat in the
1860s and, although the details above are incomplete, *Lloyd's Register of Shipping* from 1 July
1867 to 30 June 1868 gives her main dimensions, namely: length 60.0 ft, breadth 18.2 ft, and
depth of hold 10.0 ft.]

1818

No 15   A sloop built at [Countess] Wear of 85 tons call'd the *Friends,* built
for Captn P. Brown of Lewis in the County of Sussex by the same draft as No
11 with no alteration excepting 1 more ⊠ [1] aftward to make her swim more
on an even keel. She was liked extremely well, sail'd fast & carried a very
fair cargo. Should build again by the same draft with no alterations
excepting for particular purposes.
Scantling of her frame [-]

[Dimensions of] No 15

Length between the perpendiculars	[-]
Length aloft on deck	[-]
Breadth extreme	[-]

[[1]This means that an extra frame, identical to the ⊠ frame, was inserted abaft it. See Glossary:
Dead-flat, the term for the midship section or midship bend.]

Depth in the hold   [-]
  Burthen in tons 87
  Call'd the *Friends*
  Captn Peter Brown, Lewes, Sussex

1818

No 16   A brig call'd the *Exeter* built at [Countess] Wear by the same draft
as No 9 [the *Sedulous*], only with the alterations therein specefied: she was 9
inches wider, 2 [ft] 10 [inches] longer and 3 inches deeper in the hold & she
had a female bust-head & carved stern. She was as handsome a looking a
brig as was ever seen; she sailed extremely fast & stowed a great cargo. She
was made finer aft on the frames from 10 to 16 from the floor head to the first
foothook head & likewise forward a little – see the No 9 draft for the
alteration of the body plan.

Scantling of her frame [-]

[Dimensions of] No 16

	[Feet]	[inches]
Length from the fore part of the main stem to the after part of the stern post	70	9½
Breadth extreme	21	7
Depth in the hold	13	7½
Length aloft	75	00

  Burthen in tons No 143²⁰⁄₉₄
  Called the *Ex[e]ter*
  Captn Henry Jno Row, London

1818

No 17   A schooner call'd the *Three Sisters*, built at Topsham, of 125 tons,
compos'd by myself. She was a very good model, sailed extremely well &
carried a very fair cargo; if I altered her at all I should make her [with] a
little more tumble out on the bluff of the bow & a little fuller aft but very
little on both.

Scantling of her frame which *was much too large*

Sided		Moulded	
Floors	11 inches	Floors mid[ship]s 11 in., head 8 in.	
1 f[oothooks]	9½ in.	1 f[oothooks]	7 in.
2 ditto	8½ in.	2 ditto	[-]
3 ditto	7 in.	3 ditto	6¼ [in.]
Tops	6½ in.	Tops	4½ [in.]
Upper beams	10 in.	Upper beams	9 [in.] in mid [shi]ps
Lower beams	[-]	Lower beams	[-]
Knees	5½ in.		
Hooks	ditto		

[Dimensions of] No 17

	[Feet]	[inches]
Length between the perpendiculars	67	6
Length aloft on deck	69	8½
Breadth extreme	20	8

	[Feet]	[inches]
[cont'd]		
Depth in hold	12	4½

Burthen in tons No 125¹⁷/94
Call'd the *Three Sisters*
Captn Wm Languish, Weymouth

1819

No 18   A sloop call'd the *Eclipse* built to car[r]y stones from Torbay to Topsham for Robt Davy much after the plan of a barge, only narrower gangways. She answered the river as well as for the purpose she was intended for and sailed very fair.

[Dimensions of] No 18

	[Feet]	[inches]
Length from the fore part of the main stem to the after part of the stern post	54	11½
Length aloft on deck	56	1
Extreme breadth	18	0½
Depth in the hold	7	11½

Burthen in tons 76²⁰/94

Call'd the *Eclipse* – built for bring[ing] stones from Torbay (the first), built in every particular like a barge only narrow gangways.

1819

No 19   A smack call'd the *Edinburgh Castle* built for the Edinburgh and Leith Shipping Comp[an]y, Leith, drawn by Mr P. Hedderwick. She was as handsome a smack as could possibly be built in every respect and I think could not be made better by altering her in the least. She was commanded by Captn Wm Hutton; sailed very fast, particular[l]y when it blew a fresh breese [when] nothing could go from her.

1819. Dimensions of the smack *Edinburgh Castle* of Leith

	[Feet]	[inches]
Length from the fore part of the main stem to the after part of the stern post aloft is	74	11½
Length aloft on deck	80	5
Breadth extreme	24	3
Depth in the hold	12	6

Burthen in tons 188⁹⁰/94. When launched drew
8 feet 10 in. aft and 5 [feet] 6 [in.] forward,
[a difference of] 3 [feet] 4 [in.]

[See pp. 27–9 for a detailed account of timber and other materials used in her construction.]

1819

No 20   A smack or yacht called the *Regent* built for the Honr the Commissioners of the Northern Lighthouses. Drawn by myself, she was as handsome a smack as could possibly be built in every respect; she could not be altered for the better in any way. Was commanded by Captn P[eter] Soutar. She sailed remarkable fast; nothing could, when [she was] in a good trim, beat her.

[See pp. 31–3 for a detailed account of timber and other materials used in her construction. Peter Hedderwick in his *Treatise on Marine Architecture*, 1830, p. 147, supplies the following details concerning the *Regent*: tonnage 142.27, length 66 ft, breadth 22 ft 7 in., and depth of hold 11 ft 6 in. The list of subscribers to Hedderwick's book includes the name of 'Captain Peter Soutar, Regent Nor. Lt-H. Tender'.]

1819

Dimensions of the schooner *Ceres* after she was altered from a stone boat—No 12 see—on account of her being too large and not answering the purpose intended.

	[Feet]	[inches]
Length from the fore part of the main stem to the after part of the stern post	67	9
Length aloft on deck	70	4½[1]
Extreme breadth	20	4½
Depth in the hold	12	1
Burthen in tons 122⁵⁷⁄₉₄		

[1 The figure has been altered and could read 0½.]

[Undated]

Dimensions of the barge *Friends Goodwill* after she was lengthened and rose upon [frame] C.

	[Feet]	[inches]
Length from the fore part of the main stem to the after part of the stern post	53	7½
Length aloft on deck	55	7½
Breadth extreme	18	2½
Depth in the hold	7	9
Burthen in tons 75²⁰⁄₉₄		

1826

Schooner called the *Eliza* sold [to] Messrs Hemmett & Co. of Beer, April 14, 1826.

	Ft	ins
Length for ton[n]age	55	2¾
Brea[d]th extreme	18	8¼
Depth in the hold	10	3½
Length on deck	58	3
Ton[n]age 81⁷⁶⁄₉₄ tons register		

[See pp. 55–7 for very detailed dimensions of this schooner built by D. B. Davy. The *Merchants' Register of Shipping* for 1828 gives the name of her owners as Hammett.]

Brig called the *Dorothea* sold [to] Mr George Joad of London, September 24th, 1826.

	Feet	ins
Length for ton[n]age	84	9
Breadth extreme	24	4¼
Depth in the hold	15	9
Length on deck	89	0
Ton[n]age 221⁵⁶⁄₉₄ tons register		

[1827]

Schooner called the *Rose*, late the *Exeter Packet* sloop; lengthened 9 ft 6 ins, brea[d]thened 8 ins, and made from 60 tons to 88 tons register. Captn Edwd Webber master and part owner and Mr Wm Wreford owners. Dimensions when lengthened as follows.

	Ft	ins
Length for ton[n]age	62	2
Length on deck	65	1½
Tread of keel	57	1½
Brea[d]th extreme	18	0
Depth in the hold	9	9½

Register ton[n]age – 88⁴⁹⁄₉₄ tons admeasurement.
Lengthened by the day and materials charged as used.
[Signed] D. B. Davy, January 31st, 1827.

[A letter book of D. B. Davy and Company – see note on p. 67 – contains a copy of one sent to Mr John Harrison of Topsham on 8 April 1837, quoting a price of £24 10s per foot for lengthening a schooner.
We have received your note requesting to know our terms for lengthening the schooner *Fame*, also prices for the principal leading articles otherwise likely to be required for alterations & repairs found necessary, independent of the lengthening in the fore and after parts of the vessel. In giving our terms we beg to observe there are many methods of finishing jobs of this kind & we would not wish by any means to undertake it without we could do the owners justice and ourselves credit . . . £24 10s per foot for lengthening – this sum to include materials needful for so doing – to make the shifts good in every respect with proper fastenings – to caulk & finish the same complete in workmanlike manner . . .
The lengthening of small sailing vessels is touched on by Basil Greenhill in *The Merchant Schooners*, 1968 edn, vol. 1, p. 122.

Dimensions of masts, yards &c of a brig called the *Dorothea*, about 220 tons, sold to Mr George Joad of London, built by Danl B. Davy, 1826. [Last two columns record the length of the mast head or the yard arm.]

	Length	Diameter ins	Ft	ins
Main mast extreme length	60 ft by	17½ head	11	
Yard	42	10½ arm	2	
Topmast	36	11 head	4	6
Yard	32	8 arm	2	
Top gallant mast	16 to rigging	6 pole	13	
Yard	21	5½ arm	1	6
Royal yard	16	4 ditto	1	
Fore mast	56 by	17 head	10	6
Yard	41	10½ arm	2	
Topmast	35	11 head	4	6
Yard	31	8 arm	2	
Top gallant mast	15 to rigging	6 pole	12	
Yard	20	5½ arm	1	
Royal yard	15	4 ditto	1	
Bowsprit	36	17½		
Jib boom	31	9¼		
Main boom to be 6 feet over taffiel rail [taffrail]	42	10		
Gaff	28	7		
Spritsail yard	35	8		

Trysail mast from the deck to the mast head
8 studding sail booms

Dimensions of mast[s] & yards of schooner *Grace*, about 70 tons, when altered from a smack into a schooner, August 10th, 1827

		Length [Ft] [ins]		Diameter [ins]		Ft	ins
Main mast	extreme length	51	0	12	head	9	6
Fore mast	ditto	50	0	13	head	11	0
Main top mast	ditto	30	0	6	pole	6	
Fore top mast	ditto	30	0	7	pole	7	
Fore yard	ditto	35	6	7½	arm	2	
Top sail yard	ditto	26	6	6½	ditto	2	6
Top gallant yard	ditto	17	0	4½	ditto	2	
Royal yard	ditto	10	6	3½	ditto	1	6
Main boom		33	0	8			
Main gaff		22	0	6			
Fore boom		19	6	7			
Fore gaff		17	6	5			
Bowsprit		33	0	12			
2 Studding sail booms each		19	0	4			

SHIPBUILD[ER]S ADDRESSES

Lynn in Norfolk

Messrs Wales & Dobson	Lynn
Mr Richardson	ditto

Hull in Yorkshire

Mr Wm Gibson	Hull	shipbuilder
Mr Edwd Gibson	ditto	ditto
Mr Wm Glaydow [Gleadow]	ditto	ditto
Mr Thos Walton	ditto	ditto
Messrs Barns Dicks & King	[ditto]	ditto
Messrs Hall & Richerson [Richardson]	[ditto]	ditto

Timber agents at Hull

Mr Caddy, agent, High Street

Shipbuilders addresses at South Shie[l]ds & Newcastle, Northumberland-shire

Mr C. Young	shipbuilder	South Shields
Mr Straker & Company/		
Mr Raffields manager		ditto
Mr Jno Laing & Sons	ditto	South Shields
Messrs Forsyth & Co.	ditto	ditto
Messrs Wright Harle & Co.	ditto	ditto
Messrs Smyth	[ditto]	Newcastle
Messrs Ranner & Company	[ditto]	ditto
Mr Huntley	[ditto]	ditto
Mr Sleinson	[ditto]	ditto
Mr Farrenton	[ditto]	ditto

Shipbuilders addresses at Sunderland in Durhamshire

Mr Philip Laing	shipbuilder		Sunderland
Mr [Robert] Reay	ditto	Hilton [Hylton] Ferry	ditto
Messrs Wm & Jno Gales	ditto	ditto	ditto
Mr James Crone	ditto	North Shore	ditto
Mr James Hall	ditto	ditto	ditto
Mr Thomas Tiffin	ditto		Sunderland
Mr Wm Potts	ditto		ditto
Messrs Thos & Robt Davison	ditto		ditto
Mr Jno Hutchinson	ditto		ditto
Mr Thos Burn	ditto		ditto
Mr James Johnson	ditto	Deptford near	ditto
Mr Luke Crone	ditto	Monkwearmouth near	ditto
Messrs Allison's	[ditto]	ditto	ditto
Mr Jno Brown	[ditto]	ditto	ditto
Messrs Wm Adamson & Sons	[ditto]	ditto	ditto
Mr Partis Oswald	[ditto]	ditto	ditto
Messrs Davinson	[ditto]	ditto	Sunderland
Mr Thos Law	[ditto]	ditto	ditto

Timber agents at Sunderland in Durham
Mr Wm Sherlock	Monkwearmouth	near Sunderland
Mr Wm Micklan	Sunderland	
Messrs Law & Anderson	ditto	
Mr Jno Mills	ditto	
Mr Isaac Newton	ditto	
Messrs Ant[on]y Hodd & Co	ditto	and at Newcastle
Messrs Hall, Gothard & Slack	ditto	Newcastle

    [Later listed as timber agents at Newcastle and Shields]

Tanners at Shields, Newcastle & Sunderland
Messrs Harrison & Parker	Gateson [Gateshead?]near Newcastle		
Mr Thew	[tanner]		Newcastle
Mr Liddle	ditto		Newcastle
Mr Geo. Wilson	ditto		Newcastle
Mr Sellick [or Sillick]	ditto		Newcastle
Mr Richardson	ditto		North Shields
Mr [Jno] Richardson	ditto		Sunderland
Mr Jno Clark	ditto		ditto
Mr Wm Cross	ditto	Downhill near	ditto

Addresses of timber merchants who send timber at Shields, Newcastle & Sunderland &c &c
Mr Wm Sloval [or Stoval]	Petworth, Sussex
Mr Chas Childs	Warnham [Sussex]
Mr Jno Morrice	London
Mr Walter Morrice	Ealing [Eling], Hants
Mr Edwd Evershed	Shoreham, Sussex
Mr Jas Biffin & Son	Del[1] Quay, near Chichester, Sussex
Mr – Twyming	South Hampton, Hants
Mr Jas Breeds	Hastings, Sussex
Mr Thos Breeds	Hastings, Sussex
Mr Wm Upton	Petworth, Sussex
Mr Ben Hobbs	Redbridge, Hants
Mr – Newell	ditto failed lately – 1819
Messrs T., F., & S. Burnell	Fareham, Hants
Mr Smiths	Wenborn, Sussex [Wimborne, Dorset ?]
Mr Pilchard	Rye, Sussex

Boat builders at North & South Shields
Mr Jno Plats	North Shields
Messrs Morton & Thomson	ditto
Mr Crow	ditto
Mr Stevenson	ditto
Mr Oliver	South Shields
Mr Mives	ditto

    [Later described as a mast maker.]
Mr Robson	ditto

REMARKS ON DIFFERENT SUBJECTS CONCERNING SHIPS & BUILDING

GREENOCK [on the River Clyde, Scotland], September 28th, 1818

There are now just launched at Greenock [three ships], one 530 & the other two 470 tons regester. They have three tier of beams all fore & aft which is fastened with two lodging knees to each [beam?] with a stringer above & below the beams 13 inches through by 5 ins thick. The stringer is bolted through the side & likewise through the beams & clinched on the deck on a square ring; [there is] also an iron standard knee on each beam of the upper deck. Their floors were sided from 12 to 13 inches; first foothooks sided 11½ to 12 in.; keelson sided 15 in., moulded 18 in.; lower deck beams sided 12 inches, moulded 11 in.; upper deck [beams] sided 11 in., moulded 10 in. in midships, smaller fore and aft; 4–6 inch wales; 3½ inch bottom. Waterways were very thick & left round. One was built by Mr Steel & two by Mr Scott & Sons. They both built the hulls complete, [supplying] such [items] as lower deadeyes, rudder, windlass, capstern, and all carpainters work belonging to the hull; the owners finding the cabin, plumbing & painting; & the builder likewise to find mast [s] & spars with iron work complete for £12 10s per register ton. But Mr Steel says he will loose near 700£ & Mr Scott near £500 by each. They were very fine ships & I think faithfully built & fastened.

The principle [principal] builders are
Mr Steel
Mr Scott & Sons
Mr Simmings
Mr Kerswall
with two other
small ones

Mr Scoot [Scott] is worth a great deal of money, report says £150,000 They get a great deal of timber from Bideford & Malham.

[Both Robert Steele (1745–1830) and John Scott (1752–1837) were notable Clyde shipbuilders. Steele was in partnership with John Carswell from 1796 to 1816; a list of the ships built by them is given by David R. MacGregor in *Merchant Sailing ships 1775–1815* (1985 edition p. 209). The firm then became Robert Steele & Co. According to MacGregor they launched the ship *Albion* on 2 October 1818, four days after Davy set down his 'remarks'. For the original specification of the *Albion*, 505⁶⁸/₉₄ tons, see MacGregor *Merchant Sailing Ships 1815–1850* (1984), pp.45–6. The 'Mr Scott' mentioned by Davy was John Scott (ii). William Scott (ii), who was born in 1756, was associated with him in his early years, the firm being John and William Scott, but in 1802 it became John Scott & Sons as William a short time before had gone to Barnstaple, where (and also later at Bristol) he worked in the timber and shipbuilding trades: *Two Centuries of Shipbuilding by the Scotts at Greenock* (1950). Greenock subscribers to Hedderwick's *Treatise on Marine Architecture* (1830) included the shipbuilders John Scott, William Simons (? Davy's 'Mr Simmings') and Robert Carsewell (? Davy's 'Mr Kerswall') of Port Glasgow.]

Bridport [Dorset], December 7th, 1818

Mr Good has just launched a brig of about 156 tons register. He has £3000 for to build the hull complete with all carpainters & joiners work inside &

out, cabin included, mast[s], yards & all spars, sails, cordage & all other stores, fit for sea even to a tinder box & spy glass, to be copper fastened, & smiths work belonging to the hull [also included]. Mr G'd has likewise to build the hull of a brig, 153 tons register, complete & to find all carpainters & joiners work, cabin &c & to find all mast[s] & yards & s[p]ars [and] smiths work thereto belonging without any extra bill whatever for £1800, to be copper fastened & to find smiths work on the hull. Mr G'd has two smacks of about 100 tons each for a Glasgow Company for which he has £11 15 per ton to find or build the hull complete & to finish them fit for sea with all carpainters & joiners work, cabin excepted, & to find all mast[s], yards & smiths work & to be copper fastened to the wales. All Mr G'ds scantlings are nearly equal to *ours*.

[A loose sheet of paper endorsed by Danl B. Davy, January 14th, 1819, but not in his handwriting, gives prices charged or quoted by 'Boles Good', Bridport.]

Under 100 tons £12 per ton iron fastened & £12 12s per ton copper fastened, finding only the iron work attached to the hull without joiners work, pumps, plumbers or painters work. From 100–120 tons £13 iron £13 13s copper, 120–150 tons £13 10s [iron] £14 copper, 150–180 tons £15 copper fastened.

Weymouth [Dorset], December 8th, 1818

Mr Peasant [Beasant] has a brig just launched of about 150 tons; her floors are sided 12 in. to 9 in. & all her frame is very fair as well as her plank but very badly fastened: her beams and knees are of a good size, say beams sided 10 [in.], moulded 9 in., knees sided 5½ [in.]. Mr Ales of Weymouth has likewise two smack[s] of about 90 to 100 tons each; their floors are sided about 8 in. and their first foothooks 7 in. ; in fact, they have very small bad sappy frames altogether such as no one of judge[ment] would allow. For building them iron fastened & to find the hull complete with cabin and fore castle he has £10 10s per register ton.

[Thomas Ayles of Weymouth and Melcombe Regis, shipbuilder, listed as bankrupt, *Trewman's Exeter Flying-Post* 18 February 1830. Two shipbuilders are recorded at Weymouth in Pigot and Co's *Royal National & Commercial Directory*, June 1844 (Dorsetshire p.34): Thomas Ayles, Hope Quay, and Christopher Beasant, Hope Quay.]

Redbridge [on the River Test, Southampton], December 9th, 1818

Mr Ben: Hobbs has a brig of about 130 tons or thereabouts; her floors are sided 10 in., first foothooks 9 [in.], seconds 8 in., tops 6½ [in.], wales 4½ in. [He has] to find cabin, mast[s], yards with smiths work complete for [£]12 15s per ton, the hull to be copper fastened; Mr H's to find windlass, rudder, capstern &c, with iron work complete fit for sea. Mr Morrice asked him 8£ per load for timber such as would frame her.

[A note at the foot of the next page of Davy's volume states:]
Mr Hobbs lost by building Mr Kings vessel of Bristol, he says, about £500, but she had very large scantlings & was a very high long narrow ship & he was a very particular man. He had [£]13 13s per ton to find the hull complete with mast[s], yards & all joiners work except the cabin.

Hythe [on Southampton Water], December 10th, 1818

Mr Richards has a brig of about 190 tons register just launched. Her floors are sided 10 [in.], first foothooks 8½ in. ; which are very sappy as well as the rest of her frame. He has sold the hull complete for sea with all the carpainters & joiners work (cabin excepted) [and] smiths work to the hull for £11 [per ton], to be copper fastened & deck [copper nailed?]. Mr R'ds builds very slight vessels; he wont contract for one at all as he builds nothing but slops. [Slop-built: jerry built, fig. loosely built or made (*Shorter Oxford English Dictionary*). Perhaps Mr Richards re-used old timbers or plank.]
[The following two notes are on the opposite page to the Hythe entry:]
Whindfields & Thomas, Gateshead & London, firm for the Patent Iron Neck Windlass, which is a very good plan.
Builders names at Leith:
Mr Cunningham
Mr Minges
Mr Symes the principle [principal] one
[Alexander Sime, shipbuilder, Leith, is listed as a subscriber in Peter Hedderwick, *Treatise on Marine Architecture* (1830).]

Shipbuilders at Lynn in Norfolk

Messrs Wales & Dobson   shipbuilders
Mr Richardson   ditto
    These are the only respectable people in the place to do business with safely. Messrs Wales & Co bought 10 of the keel pieces that Parker[1] took there at 3s 6d per foot and are going to write about some oak timber and plank.
[[1]Possibly Captain Thomas Parker, master of Robert Davy's schooner *Ceres* (*Lloyd's Register of Shipping* for 1820).]

Hull, June 10th, 1819 – Kingston on Hull

June 10th – An account of ships building, builders &c &c
Mr Edwd Gibson is now building a ship of about 500 tons for an extra East Indiaman; her frame is very good and nearly on the whole as large scantlings as we should put. She is to have no wood knees but a thick stringer or waterway, above and below the beam, into which the beams are to be dovetailed as likewise bolted through the side – up and down ways through the whole, and coak'd into the stringers with an iron hanging knee to each beam, canted a little. He informed me according to the price of timber and the quantity she had consumed he could not afford her for less then £16 per register ton fit[t]ed out in every respect much as we do with every thing belonging to the hull as a shipwright, cabin, painting & plumbing excepted. I mentioned to him respecting supplying him twith [with] oak timber from our quarter but by his account of the price he obtained it at he got it almost as cheap as we do in our yard. He says he can get very good sizeable timber fit for vessel[s] from 250 to 500 tons register for about from £7 to £7 10s per ton girt measure. He has a very fine dock and

repairs a good many vessels; otherwise what new ships he builds he would be looseing a great deal of money by at the price he get[s] which is from £12 12s to [£]13 13s per ton for vessels from 300 to 500 tons.

Mr Wm Gibson, his father, has been building a vessel of about 380 tons register which he has had in hand for these last two years & not being able to sell her he now intends fit[t]ing her out himself and I think would accept an offer of £12 per register ton very readily. She is not a handsome vess[e]l, neither do they build sightly vess[e]ls generally at Hull. Mr Wm Gibson and his son are both very respectable men and report says worth a good deal of money. The large ship Mr Gibson Jun is about has a top gallar'd [galleried] forecastle, poop, head, gallaries and 3 tier of beams.

Mr Wm Gleadow and Son, shipbuilders, Hull, are very respectable money'd men. They are now building a vessel of about 300 tons register on speculation which th[e]y have had in hand some considerable time, not being able to obtain a purchaser; but I dont think they know so well what new ships cost them as they attend chiefly to repairs, which is the case with all the builders at Hull. I spoke to them likewise about the elm, as also concerning sending oak timber but found the price the[y] obtained it for down the rivers from Stafford and Yorkshire, having but little or no opposition at the sales, was as cheap as we could render it ourselves into our yard and full as large scantlings. The Navy people not taking any for the dock yards from this quarter and the timber merchants agreeing altogether they get the timber almost at their own prices to what we can do in our quarter.

Mr Thos Walton, shipbuilder, Hull, is a respectable man and worth money. He is building a vess[e]l of about 300 tons register on speculation which I rather think he would be glad to sell for £13 per ton. She is not by any means a handsome vessel but quite on the contrary being very unfair and as full as possible; which is generally the case although they put good work on them. He would say nothing about the elm keel pieces or respecting any oak timber, as he said he could obtain it as cheap as we could and larger sizes then I mentioned which was from 10 to 15 feet meeting. He said he could get such size timber for [£]6 10s [per ton] girt measure.

Messrs Barns Dickes & King, Hull shipbuilders, are very respectable people although not men of such real property as the others. They are building 3 small vessels of about 130 tons for the Oporto trade, schooners for which the[y] obtain to fit them with windlass & hanging companion skylight, chain plates &c, joiners work belonging to the hull, cabin excepted, the hull fi[t]ted and finished by them much on the same plan as we do for £13 per register ton, which is considered a pritty good price there. I call'd on him about the keel pieces but he was not in any want, having given an order for the elm he should want for the vessels he was building some little time before. He came on board and looked at them and was very well pleased with the quality. He said if he had not given an order he would have endeavoured to have purchased; but generally speaking there is no dependance on the Hull people when you bring any article to find a market. They will play a long time about it and say they will come &c and in the end if not very much in want (without you will almost give it them) will not come at last. I would by no means send any thing at Hull on speculation without having an absolute bargain made before hand.

Messrs Hall & Richerson [Richardson], Hull shipbuilders, are very respectable money'd men. They are going to decline. I call'd on them about the keel pieces but they were not inclined to do any business. Indeed, by their account also, timber can be got as cheap in their neighbourhood as in ours. They say their timber last year cost them no more in the yard than from £7 to £7 10s per ton girt measure and would average from 20 to 30 feet in a tree. They say none of the builders (excepting Messrs Barns Dicks & King) at Hull seldom or ever build any vessel less than 200 tons register but generally much larger, for which they obtain for the hull complete as shipwrights, without plumbing, painting or joiners work even to the hull, for they generally never even put round a moulding at their expence, for £12 per ton to £13 copper fastened, which is the general rate that the builders are doing business for. They put nearly as much timber and plank as we do generally speaking but not quite so square sided and are not so particular about the shifts or scarfs of the timbers. The plank of the bottom they put on very irregular round the bows. The builders likewise get a great deal of timber from Nottenhamshire down through canals and likewise a great deal by canals from Stafford and Yorkshire and likewise down the Goss [? Ouse] & Trent which are branches of the Humber and lead upwards of 60 miles up.

Different memorandoms made at Hull,
June 12th 1819, by Danl B. Davy

Mr Sleinson [?Steinson] shipbuilder at Hull failed; his stock in trade was sold off during my stay which real[is]ed pritty well according to the times which were very bad. He was very much involved with Messrs Stanaford [Staniforth] & Blunt, bankers and merchant[s], owing to their failure; but he conducted his business very wild and used to drink a great deal and build at low prizes [prices] such as from £9 to £11 per ton for vessels from 200 to 400 tons; which was greatly his ruin. He was said to be worth at one time near 15 to 20,000 £.

[A Thomas Steemson was in business at Paull, east of Hull on the Humber Bank: information supplied by Mr Arthur Credland, Hull Docks Museum.]

Mr Caddy is a timber agent at Hull.

Mr Geo. Holdon & Son & Company will inqu[i]re if written to concerning the price of timber but must have the dimensions &c before they can say any thing about it as it will be useless for them to say any thing about it without having particular instructions; but oak plank of long lengths is the only thing in the timber way likely to sell to any advantage at Hull and then there must be an agreement made before hand, otherwise it will never answer.

Mr Pilchard, timber merchant, Ryde [Rye], Sussex, sends a good deal of plank but never before its agreed for before [being] shipped. There are timber merchant[s] who have yards at Morbath & Slockath where the Hull shipbuilders get a great deal of timber from about 40 miles up the river Humber.

[Morbath and Slockath (or Stockath) cannot be traced in gazetteers. Perhaps Davy is here referring to the villages of Morton and East and West Stockwith on the banks of the Trent near Gainsborough.]

Hull – on the River Humber
1819

There is a very large trade to Greenland from Hull, upward of 60 sail of vessels, which is averaged to employ near 6000 sailors; there is likewise a good West India and they are going to establish an East India trade. Their trade to the Baltic is likewise very large.

The docks at Hull are very good and will contain a great ma[n]y sail of vessel. The river Humber exceeds the Thames for depth of water and convenience of get[t]ing up and down, but is a very expensive port for ships, the dues being very heavy &c &c. The town its self is but errigular [irregularly] built excepting the west part where there are many good regular streets generally occupied by the merchants. There is a light at [the] entrance [of the river] call'd the Spurn which is a mark for a sand which runs 6 miles off and is 5 mil[e]s long, dry a[t] low water; the tide flows upwards of 24 feet at the springs.

There has been a great deal more timber fell[ed] then is commoning [than is commonly] thrown this year in York, Norfolk, Suffolk & Staffordshire; which has glutted the Hull market.

South [Shields], North Shields & Newcastle on the River Tyne, June 14th, 1819

Different shipbuilders, remarks on ditto &c

Shipbuilders at South Shields
Mr C. Young – wrote to about trennals [treenails]
Mr Raffield (Streker & Co., principles [principals])
Mr Jno Laing & Son – wrote to ditto
Messrs Forsyth & Company
Messrs Wright, Harle & Company – wrote to ditto

Prizes [prices] given at Hull, Newcast[le], Shields, Sunderland

Plank	s	
2 inches thick	£12 0	Oak from 18 to 30 ft
2½	12 0	meetings £7 10 [s].
3	12 10	Tree nails 50s to 60s
4	13 0	per thousand.
5 and upwards	14 0	Keel pieces 3s 6d per foot
		oak and elm callaper,
		to be delivered at their yard.

Mr C. Young, shipbuilder, So[uth] Shields, is a very money'd man. I call'd on him but he did not want any keel pieces. I likewise told him we could supply him with oak timber & plank &c. He was not in want for the present. I said I would take the liberty of writing him at some future time, which he was very agreeable of, and [he] said he would as soon do business with us as any other person if we would do it on as good terms, which I assured him we would; but I understand he is a very disagreeable man to do business with as he will, if there is the least opportunity, make objections and cause disputes after he has got your property. Mr Devey tells me this which I believe to be correct. If we engage to take coals of him we must be mindful to be particular to state what quality and the pit he must send it from.

Mr Raffield, active agent to Messrs Straker & Company. They are very respectable money'd men. (I call on them) or [rather upon] Mr Raffield who conduct[s] the business. He would have nothing to say about the keel pieces as he had a stock by him. I informed him about our supplying him with oak timber, plank, treenails &c. I thought he appeared inclined to do business with us at some future day. I promised to write him, stating our prizes [prices]; I also left them with him as near as I could judge. He would at any time allow us to land timber on his quay by paying 1s per load the first month and 6d for every month after and would endeavour to sell it for us if we would send it for sale but this without an engagement. I should not be inclined to do [this]; they are all such illiberal people and will take the advantage after you have sent it.

Mr Jno Laing & Sons are respectable money'd people. I call'd on them about the keel pieces which they came and looked at but [they] did not like them, not being square enough and, being to[o] crooked, would not run all their lengths they were sided. They said likewise they were to[o] small – pieces sided from 10½ to 13 [in.] suited this port best as they do not build or repair ships small enough to take them – and that October is the best months [month] to send them for sale as the Winter season is the time they are generally consumed. I left them our address respecting supplying them with oak timber, plank, treenails &c.; they were not in want and complained of the times. I said – which they were agreeable to – that I would write them when I got home stating particularly our prizes [prices] and I think if we will supply them as cheat [cheap] as theirs they will [have] no objection in doing business with us at some future period. They said they had been buying for £6 per load.

Messrs Forsyth & Company are very respectable money'd men. I call'd about the keel pieces but they wanted none for the present. I left our address in case he should want any oak timber, plank, treenails &c, which he said he should have no objection in doing in case we would let him have it as cheap as theirs. I promised to write him when I got home stating our prizes [prices]. He said he could get timber here for £6 per ton callaper & keel pieces at 3s per foot – he is not a very civil man to converse with.

Messrs Wright, Harle & Co. are very respectable men and worth money. I called but they were not in want of any keel pieces and would say nothing about them. I left our address in case they should want any oak timber, plank, treenails &c &c which they said they would as soon buy of us as another if we could send it as cheap as theirs, but our price was to[o] high. I said – which they were agreeable to – that I would write them when I got home, giving them our exact prizes [prices]. They had a very large stock on hand which they got out of Norfolk & Suffolk. Some of it, large Navy timber, came from Lord [blank] [blank] Park. They bought it deliver[e]d into their yard girt measure for £8 15s per load such as Mr Morrice would be glad to take of us at their last years prizes [prices].

Tanners at Newcastle, Shields &c &c

Messrs Harrison & Parker	Newcastle, Gateson [Gateshead?]
Mr Thew	ditto
Mr Liddle	ditto
Mr Geo Wilson	ditto
Mr – Sillick	ditto
Messrs Richar[d]son's & Co.	North Shields
Mr Jno Clark	Sunderland
Mr Holmes	Hull
Mr Wm Cross	Downhill near Sunderland
Mr Jno Richardson	Sunderland

Mr Caddy, timber agent, Hull

Mr Stoval, timber merchant a[t] Petworth in Sussex, sends *a great deal* of oak timber, plank &c at Sunderland [and] Shields & has a good deal there now for sale, more than is required. He keeps an agent there call'd Mr Jno Drydon who lives at South Shields.

Mr Smith, timber merchant, Wembourn [Wimborne], Dorsetshire, send[s] a good deal of timber at Sunderland &c &c. He has at present 40 or 50 keel pieces laying at South Shields for sale which have been there some time – he keeps an agent call'd [blank].

Mr Pilchard, timber merchant, Ryde [Rye], Sussex, send[s] a great deal at Sunderland, Shields &c.

Boat builders at South Shields &c &c

Mr Jno Plats	North Shields
Messrs Morton & Thomson	ditto
Mr Crow	ditto
Mr Stevenson	ditto
Mr Oliver	South Shields
Mr Robson	ditto
Mr Mives mast maker	ditto

Mr – Childs, timber merchant of Arundel in Sussex, send[s] a good deal of timber at Sunderland, Shields &c – he likewise keeps an agent there call'd Mr Thos Hall who lives at South Shields.

Mr Wm Shalock [Sherlock], timber agent, Monkwearmouth near Sunderland – respectable but not any property.

Mr Wm Mickland – timber agent, Sunderland.

Messrs Law & Anderson, timber agents, Sunderland, are very respectable moneyed men.

Mr Jno Mills, timber agent, Sunderland.

Mr Isaac Newton, timber agent, Sunderland, is a very respectable man.

Messrs Ant[on]y Hodd & Co. do business both at Sunderland, Newcastle & Shields. They are very respectable people and do business on commissions for £3 per cent not ensuring [insuring] bad debts, and £5 per cent ensuring [insuring] bad debts, which is the regular mode with them and Messrs Law & Anderson, but no other agent there do insure bad debts but they & them. The regula[r] comm[issio]n is £3 per cent.

Different timber merchants who send timber at Shields, Newcastle, Sunderland &c &c &c

		Agents	
Mr Wm Sloval [or Stoval]	Petworth, Sussex		
Mr Chas Chield	Warnham	Thos Hall	South Shields
Mr Jno Morrice	London	Messrs Law & Anderson	
Mr Walter Morrice	Eling	ditto	ditto
Mr Edwd Evershed	Shoram [Shoreham], Sussex		
Mr Jas Baffin & Sons	Del[l] Quay		
Mr – Twyming	South Hampton		
Mr Jas Breads	Hastings, Sussex		
Mr Thos Breads	ditto ditto		
Mr Wm Upton	Petworth, Sussex		
Mr Ben Hobbs	Redbridge		
Mr Newell	ditto (just failed)		
Mr Pilchard	Rye, Sussex		
Mr Smith	Wenborn [Wimborne]		

Messrs Hall Gothard & Slack, timber agents at Newcastle & Shie[l]ds, are very respectable people. They insure bad debts for £5 per cent but their regular commission is £3. They some time purchas[e] timber on their own account.

Mr Angus & Company, coach builders, St Johns Lane, Newcastle, will buy any elm board, spokes, nail stocks &c if we will send him a sample first for him to see how he likes them. His prizes [prices] are as follows viz:

Hind spoke, 30 inches long, 2½ in. broad ditto ⎫
Fore spoke, 20 inches long, 2½ in. broad ditto ⎬ oak [No price given]
Nail stocks, 11½ inches long, 10½ inches through ⎭ 1s 9d each
ditto ditto, 11 in. long, 9 inches through   1s 6d each
ditto ditto, 10 in. long, 8 in. through   1s 3d each

They will take if they like the sample 1500 of ¾ in. elm board, 1000 ft of 1 in. ditto, 2000 of the spokes & 300 nail stocks or knaves

July 21st, 1819

Prizes [prices] that Mr Wm Sherlock had been obtaining about 2 or 3 months since for timber &c

Oak timber from 15 to 20 feet meeting callaper per ton – 50 feet – £7 10s.

Oak plank

		s
2 inch oak plank per load	£12	10
2½ in. ditto	13	10
3 in. ditto	14	10
4 in. ditto	15	10
5 in. ditto and upwards	16	10

Keel pieces well sided 4s per foot

[Margin] Keel pieces of unequal siding are measured by the inverted line

Tree nails

12 inch tree nails	£2 per thousand/ 1000	
15 in. ditto	£3	ditto
18 in. ditto	£4	ditto
21 in. ditto	£5	ditto
24 in. ditto	£6	ditto

3 & 4 inch beach [beech] plank £7 10s per load

Different coals that will suite Topsham

Fawcett Main	Sunderland		price	25s 6d
Herriton Main	ditto			23s 6d
Bun Moor	ditto	burn white		22s 5d
Eaden Main	ditto			27s
South Main	ditto	large but burn white		21s
Russels High Main	ditto			24s
Russels Main	ditto	large but burn white		22s
Washington Main	ditto			21s
Boutley Walsend	ditto			21s
Branell Main	Shields or Newcastle			22s 6d
Gleb Main	ditto or ditto			22s

2¼ quarters coals to the chaldron
17 & a keel makes out 17 chaldron
Winchester measure to the keel
38¼ quarters to the keel of coals
Duty 6s per chaldron
1820

Ship builders at Dartmouth, Devon

Mr Wm Matthews
Mr John Gibbs
Mr Newman   }   7 vessels building at this time; price for
Mr Page   building as near as I could find about £10
Mr Nichols   to £10 10s per ton copper fastened
Mr Follett   [Signed] D. B. Davy, 1819

[Pigot and Co's *London and Provincial New Commercial Directory* for 1823–4 lists three shipbuilders at Dartmouth: Wm Follett, Undercliff; George Gibbs, Coombe; and Wm Matthews, Coombe.]

[Guernsey shipbuilders]

[Letter endorsed by D. B. Davy:] 1827. Shipbuilders at Guernsey with their general characters given me by Mr Cox of Topsham.

           Fore Street, Topsham, Monday
Saml Browns respects to Mr Cox.

As he wishes to know the ship–builders names in the Island of Guernsey, shall deleniate them as under.

Berry Le Patourel, who has built (among others) some ships for London merchants greatly to their satisfaction for the East India free trade &c.

Alexander Thom, (a Scotsman) who first came to the island carpenter of a ship, when I was a boy, & first taught the islanders to build large vessells, & (I think) now builds the best, but, who, through the liberallaty of sentiments, and having been sur[r]ounded by pretended friends or, blood suckers rather, together with a want of education, has unfortunately failed, but is now going on.

John Vaudin   }   South Beach are constantly
Thos de la Mare }   building
Wm Jones, South Beach, also builds. The others are of no note.

[There is a further endorsement by D. B. Davy, stating that he had written to Alexr Thom, Mr Will Jones and Mr John Vaudin, 13 September 1827.]

[The names of four full-rigged ships, twenty-six brigs and three schooners built on the island between 1 January 1815 and 1 January 1828 are recorded on page 456 of Jacob's *Annals of Guernsey* (1830). All thirty-three of these were launched by the shipbuilders mentioned in this letter: ten by Le Patourel, another ten by Alexander Thom, eight by de la Mare, four by Vaudin and one by Jones. Le Patourel, whose christian name is given as Barry, built the first of these, the 140-ton brig *Belle Alliance*. Crowds of people watched her launching at Glategny, including the Lieutenant-Governor, Sir John Doyle, who presented her with an ensign (see Victor Coysh, 'The Guernsey Shipbuilding Industry', *Transactions of La Societe Guernesiaise*, 1952 p. 212). Alexander Thom launched the second, a 250-ton full-rigged ship, the *Alexander* from the yard at Long Store the same year; another ship, the *Sophia*, 208 tons, in 1817 and a third, the *Caledonia*, in 1819. A second list in Jacob's *Annals* (p. 457) gives the names of thirty-five 'cutter-built vessels', seven of which were launched by William Jones. A note states that many vessels were sent from Guernsey to England to be repaired previous to 1812.]

1827

Mr Robt Bruce, Leith }	Leith & Edinburgh Shipping Company, Leith, managed by Mr Robt Bruce
Mr Crighton, Leith }	Manager of the Edinburgh & London Shipping Company, Leith
Captn Gourley, Leith }	Manager of the Old Shipping Company, Leith
Mr D. Elmslie, Aberdeen }	Manager of the Aberdeen & London Shipping Co., Aberdeen
Chas White, Esqr, Cannon Wharf, London }	Manager of the Cannon Company

Memorandum November 3rd, 1821

It took a smith called Storm [or Sturm] who worked in our own shop at Topsham 6 days to make 9 fathom or 54 feet of ⅝ inch chain cable, so according to this calculation it will take 4 weeks work for a man (to do nothing else) to make 35 fathom, the length of a stone boats chain cable. We gave him 12s per week,

say 4 weeks work at 12s per week	£2	8s	0
Weight of 35 fathom of ⅝ inch chain cable is about Cwt 7 3qrs 0lbs, say prime cost of ditto in the shop brought from Wales 12s per cwt with all expences included }	4	13	0
Coals in making ditto, say 4 bushill per week – 2 quarters at 10s }	1	0	0
	£8	1	0

54 feet of ⅝ inch chain weighs about cwt 1 3 10
If I can get 50s per cwt saying it [35 fathom] would weigh cwt 7 3 0 it would come to £19 7 6 and it could be made according to the present price of iron and labour very well for about £8 72 6d, leaving a profit of, say, £11 0 0 for rent &c &c I&c &c
[Signed] Danl B. Davy October [?]3, 1821

[The name Sturm occurs in the Topsham parish registers; there is, for example, an entry recording the marriage of Frederick William Sturm, blacksmith, and Mary Anne Bird on 25 December 1823.]

[MATERIALS AND COSTS OF INDIVIDUAL VESSELS]

An account of timber, plank &c used in a schooner [called the *Three Sisters*] of 125 tons register, January 14, 1819, which was built & the quantity known to be correct.

Oak timber

	[Feet]	[inches]
Floors	481	5
First foothooks	503	1
Second ditto	448	3
Third & tops	776	8
Beams, knees &c	1616	6

£ s

Feet 3825 11 at 3s [per foot] 573 18

Oak plank used inside & out

	Feet	in.	Feet	in.	
6 inch	17	6	8	9	solid
5½ in.	52	7	23	9	ditto
5 in.	82	8	45	10	ditto
4½ in.	565	5	211	6	ditto
4 in.	90	4	30	1	
3½ in.	565	6	195	0	
3 in.	1587	6	380	2	
2½in.	3863	10	805	2	
2 in.	843	6	140	6	
1½ in.	131	10	16	6	

50/1857 3

37 7 3 at £10 [per load] 371 8 = £945 6

Brought up [top of next page] £945 6[s]

Elm plank used

4 inch	219	4	73	0	solid
3 inch	815	2	203	9	solid

50/276 9

5 26 9 at £6 = 33 4 10

Fir plank used [for the] deck &c

2½ in.	754	10	157	1	solid
2 in.	485	8	92	0	ditto
1½ in.	99	2	11	4	ditto

50/260 5

5 10 5 at £10 = 52 2 0

Elm timber 135 1			
Fir timber 52 9	at 2s	13 11 0	
Treenails used 4,000	at 3s	7 18 7	
Deal used by the joiners not extra	at 63s	12 12 0	
		16 15 5	= 135 19 10

24

	[Cwt	qrs	lbs]							
Oakham [oakum] used	7	2	0	at 22s	8	5	0			
Tar 3 barrels				at 24s	3	12	0			
Pitch	4	0	0	at 12s	2	8	0			
Iron spike nails	5	2	0	at 25s	6	17	6			
Iron used on sundry										
jobs 1 [Ton]	14	3	13	at 42s	73	4	4			
Copper fastenings	11	0	24	at 16 [?]	84	14	8			
Copper rings					3	10	0 =	182	11	6

carried over			£1263	16 10
Brought over			£1263	16 10
Builders labour 125 tons at 30s	187	10	0		
Joiners labour on sundry jobs } cabin excepted	15	13	7		
Caulkers labour 125 tons at 3s 3d	20	6	3 =	223	9 10
This money she real[l]y cost [illegible] as I built				1487	6 8
the hull for £10 per ton, 125 tons at £10 =				1250	– –
Actual lost by building her				£ 237	6 8

Scantlings

Sided		Moulded	
Floors	11 inches midships	Floors	11 inches
1 foothooks	9½ to 10	1 foothooks	7½
2 ditto	8½	2 ditto	7
3 ditto	7	3 ditto	6½
Tops	6	Tops	4¾
Upper beams	10 midships	Beams	9 in. midships
Knees	5½		

This schooner was built and an exact account kept of every thing that was used in her belonging to the shipwright work & materials which is before spicefied [specified]. The cabin was found by us but is not charged in this account. Painting and plumbing was found by the owner.

January 14, 1819

Topsham   [Signed] D. B. Davy

An account of timber, plank &c &cs that would be used in a ship of about 430 tons register, January 16th, 1819, D. B. Davy.

Oak timber	Number	Feet	in.
Floors	37	1072	6
1 foothooks	100	1700	0
2 ditto	100	850	0
3 ditto	100	700	0
Long tops	102	850	0
Short tops	112	560	0
		5732	6

[cont'd]	Number	Feet	in.
Sundry pieces oak timber			
Beams upper & lower	67	2263	0
Knees	260	1300	0
Knight heads	8	310	0
Stern posts, keelson &c &cs		473	0
Hooks, transoms, long &			
short stem timbers		344	7
Pointers, crutches, bit[t]s &c &cs		154	6
Windlass pillers &c &c		364	7
Stantions, rails &[c]		170	6
Deadwood		195	0
Rudder		136	0
Carlings, ledges & framing of decks		680	0
Catheads		40	0

$$40\overline{)12163\quad 8}$$

	Feet	in.		£	s	d
carried up	304	3	8 at £8 = [£]	2432	14	8

Brought up				2432	14	8
	Feet	in.				
Keel	170	0 at 2s 6d		21	0	0
False keel	100	0 at 1s		5	0	0
Hatches				5	0	0
Head & galleries				150	0	0
Treenails	12,000	at 63s		37	16	0
				2651	10	8

	[Cwt	qrs	lbs]		£	s	d
Oakham [oakum] at 22s	40	0	0		44	0	0
Tar 15 barrels at 26s					19	10	0
Pitch	25	0	0	at 14s	17	10	0
Iron eight tons at 30s					240	0	0
Shipwrights labour	£	s	d				
430 tons at 30s	645	0	0				
Joiners labour	60	0	0				
Caulkers labour							
430 tons at 4s 6d	96	15	0				
Launching the ship & use							
of materials	20	0	0	=	821	15	0
Copper fastenings							
430 tons at 15s					322	10	0

carried over				£4116	15	8

Brought over   £4116 15 8
Oak & elm plank used
  inside & out   Solid feet
6 inch plank   1140 superficial 570 0
5 in. ditto   456   ditto   190 0
4½in. ditto   720   ditto   270 0
4 in. ditto   2672   ditto   882 0
3in.   ditto   15054   ditto   3763 0
                              ———————
                        50/5675 0

              load   113 25 10 at £13   £1475   0 0
Deal plank for decks
3 in. plank 6660 superficial   1665 0
4 in. ditto waterways 260 ditto   86 8
                              ——————
                        50/1751 8

                        35 1 8   at £12   420   0 0
                                              ——————————
                                               £6011   0 0
To build the hull for £14   430 tons
  per ton register   6020   0 0
                                              ——————————
        Profit   £   9   0 0

A vessel to these dimensions could not be
built for less to get any thing by it for per ton 15 to 16£.

Scantlings
  Sided
Floors   13 inches by 13 in. & 21 feet long
1 foothooks   11½ in.   Stem   14 in.
2 ditto   10 in.   Keel   13 in. square
3 ditto   9½ in.   Keelson   14 by 16 in.
Long tops   8 in.   Stern post 14 in.
Short tops   7½ in.   Transom   12 to 9½ in.
Upper beams   9 in.   Hooks   11 in.
Lower beams   12½in.   Knees upper deck 5½ in., lower 7 inches
This calculation is quite, I believe, correct; but no ship has been built so as
to keep an exact account yet,
                        December 24, 1818   [Signed] D. B. Davy

An account of timber, plank &c used in a smack of 189 tons register call'd
Edinburgh Castle, June 2nd 1819, which was built at Topsham and the exact
quantity known to be correct.

Oak timber   Feet inches
26 floors   22 feet   567 9
58 1 foothooks   11 6   665 0
73 2   ditto   7 6   548 2
169 3 ditto & tops 4 9   734 7
                          ——————
                          2515 6

[cont'd]	Feet	inches		
26 cant timbers	218	9		
35 beams	656	8		
5 transoms	80	1		
– stem post &c &c	56	3		
13 knight heads	230	8		
Keelson, deadwood &c	311	0		
Quarter timbers, knees &c	146	6		
5 breast hooks &c	66	3		
Stantions, timber heads	170	0		
95 knees	245	1		
Chocks &c &c	75	11		
Windlass	27	7		
Rudder	38	10		
Carlings, ledges &c	160	0		
Certain pieces	128	5 = 40/5127 6 at 3s 6d		

128 7 6   [£]897 6 3

Brought up   £897 6 3

Feet inches

Elm timber   40/265 1   at 2s 6d   33 2 6

6 25

Oak plank

Inch	feet	inches		Feet	inches
6	39	1	superficiale	19	6
5½	132	0	ditto	60	6
5	186	8	ditto	77	9
4½	729	9	ditto	273	7
4	829	8	ditto	276	6
3½	560	8	ditto	163	6
3	4365	7	ditto	1091	3
2½	1449	11	ditto	302	0
2	1765	5	ditto	294	3
1½	99	8	ditto	12	5 = 50/2571 3

51 21 at £12 =   617 1 0

Elm Plank
Inch

3¼   814 9   220 6 = 4 20 at   £8   36 0 0

Fir plank
Inch

3	1246	10	311	6
2½	37	3	7	9
2	927	4	154	6
1½	62	0	7	9 = 50/ 481 6

9 31 at £12 =   116 4 10

[£]1699 14 7

To brought over   £1699 14 7

Joiners deal used

Inch	feet	inches		£	s	d		
1½ deal	294	0	at 7½d	9	3	9		
1	278	0	at 5d	5	15	10		
Scantling	125	0	at 3[d]	1	11	3		
Joiners labour				24	2	0 =	40	12	10
Treenails 7,500			at 63s	23	12	6		

	[Cwt	qrs	lbs]						
Oakham	11	0	0	at 24s	13	4	0		
Tar – 1 barrel					1	8	0		
Pitch	3	0	24	at 12s	1	18	6		
Wedges 7,300				at 10s	3	13	4		
Rosin	2	2	0	at 12s	1	10	0		
Iron nails	5	0	0	at 25s	6	5	0		
Iron gross 4[Tons]	0	0	0	at £30	120	0	0 =	171	11	4
Copper fastenings								232	3	9
Shipwrights labour	189	tons		at 30s	283	10	0		
Caulkers ditto [ditto]				at 3s	28	17	0=	312	7	0

                                                            2456 9 6
To building the hull 189 tons at £12 6s [per ton]   =   2324 14 0

                                          Lost   £ 131 15 6

Built for the Leith & Edinburgh Shipping Company, Leith, in 1819.

[Loose paper] An account of timber, plank & materials expended on the barge *Eclipse* building by Mr Bishop at Gulpit [1819], labour &c included.

Oak timber	Feet	in.		Feet	in.
25 floors	6	8	in each	166	8
78 first foothooks	5	0	in each	390	0
50 second foothooks	2	7	in each	130	0
76 thirds & tops	2	6	in each	190	0
				876	8
10 stern timbers				23	6
4 transoms				30	6
– stem & knightheads				70	0
– stern post				18	0
– keelson & deadwood				69	0
13 beams	16ft by 9½ in. – 10 feet in each			130	0
46 knees	1[ft] 6[in.] in each			69	0
4 hooks	5[ft] 0[in.] in each			20	0
14 carlings	1 foot in each			14	0
48 ledges	6 inches in each			24	0
– mast step				4	0
– main hatch carling	16 by 7 inches			5	5

		Feet	in.
[cont'd]			
– paul bit [pawl bitt]	15 by 12 in.	15	0
– windlass		12	0
– windlass bit[t]s & knees		8	0
– whelps & pauls [pawls]		6	0
– hatch combings [coamings]	46 feet by 7 inches	15	6
– rails both sides	116 feet by 7 inches	33	2
– stern transom	14 by 7 in.	4	9
– chock behind the rudder case		2	0
– quarter pieces		5	0
– channels	14 by 9	7	10
– rudder		23	0
– gripe		4	6
– stantions, quarter knees, short timber heads &c		106	3

                                            1597 1

                       at 3s 6d   £279 9 6

To brought over   £279 9 6

		[Square] Feet in.	[Cubic] Feet in.
To 3½ in. wales plank superficial		157 0	solid 45 9
,, 3 in. waterways & gangways	ditto	188 0	ditto 47 0
,, 2½ in. topsides	ditto	157 0	ditto 32 0
,, 2in. bottom & ceiling	ditto	4230 0	ditto 705 0

                                 4732   40/829 9

                              20 29 9 at £11 =228 5 0

Deal plank

To 3 in. deal for rudder case

& wedges for mast	23 0	solid 5 9
,, 2½ in. ditto for quarter, forecastle, & cabin decks	610 0	solid 127 1
,, 1 in. ditto for hatches & bulwarks	426 0	solid 35 6

                                40/168 4

                              4 8 4 at £11= 46 4 0

	Cwt	qr	lbs					
To treenails 2750 at 63s [per thousand]						8	13	3
,, oakham	5	0	0	at 22s		5	10	0
,, tar 2 barrels				at 24s		2	8	0
,, pitch	3	0	0	at 12s		1	16	0
,, nails	4	0	0	at 26s		5	4	0
,, iron for fastenings				at 12s per ton 76 tons	45	12	0
,, shipwrights labour	76 tons			at 30s		114	0	0
,, joiners labour						15	0	0
,, caulkers labour	76 tons			at 3s		11	8	0
,, launching &c						5	5	0
						768	14	9

By 76 tons at £10 per ton £760 0s 0d

An account of timber, plank &c &c used on a smack or yacht of 142 tons register call'd the *Regent* which was built for the Honr Commissioners of the Northern Lighthouses, at [of] Leith, an[d] the exact quantity know[n] to be correct, Topsham, October 2nd, 1819. [Signed] Danl B. Davy

Oak timber	Feet	inches	
25 floors	383	4	
62 first foothooks	516	10	
82 second foothooks	534	10	
148 thirds, tops &c	485	3	
	1920	3	
29 beams	364	6	
44 stantions	99	1	
78 knees	157	11	
43 carlings	61	9	
73 ledges	35	3	
11 knight head[s] &c	137	5	
11 transoms, post &c	102	5	
20 stem timbers &c	103	0	
9 keelson & deadwood	193	0	
7 rudder &c &c	39	6	
33 chocks	148	6	
19 certain pieces	109	3	
6 breasthooks	55	3	= 3527 1 at 3s 6d [£]617 4 6

To brought up	oak 3527 1	at 3s 6d	£617 4s 6d
Elm timber	167 7	at 2s 6d	20 19 1
Oak plank			

	feet	in	solid					
6½ in. oak plank	7	1	=	3 9				
5½ in. ditto	59	3	=	27 1				
4½ in. ditto	541	7	=	203 0				
4 in. ditto	268	10	=	89 7				
3½ in. ditto	492	11	=	143 9				
3 in. ditto	1662	10	=	415 8				
2½ in. ditto	2657	2	=	553 6				
2 in. ditto	2622	8	=	427 1 =	50/1863 5	at £12	447 2 4¾

37 13

		solid						
3 in. elm plank	320	8 = 50/80	2 =	1 30	at [£]7	11 4 0

load feet

2½ in. fir plank	1234	0 = 50/257	1[=]	5 7	at [£]12	61 13 7½
2 in. ditto	842	7 = 50/140	5 =	2 40	at [£]12	33 12 0
1¼ in. ditto	55	0 at 6d			at 6d	1 7 6
3 in. deal for the joiners			30	0	at 1s 6d	2 5 0
1½ in. ditto for ditto			280	0	at 9d	10 10 0
1 in. ditto for ditto			374	0	at 6d	9 7 0
½ in. ditto for ditto			320	0	at 3d	4 0 0

carried over	£1219 5 1½

To brought over				£1219 5 1½
		Cwt qrs lb		
” copper fastenings under the wales	13	2 17	at 17d	108 6 1
” treenails 8060			at 80s	32 4 9
” ditto wedges 6500			at 5s	1 12 0
” wedges 26 dozen			at 2s	2 12 0
” oakham	7	2 0	at 25s	9 7 6
” tar 2 barrels			at 24s	2 8 0
” pitch	3	0 0	at 12s	1 16 0
” nails	6	0 0	at 26s	7 16 0
	[Ton cwt qrs lbs]			
” iron fastenings exactly	1	8 0 23	at 42s	58 4 7½
” shipwrights labour		142 tons	at 35s	248 10 0
	Robt Drake makes[1]			
” joiners labour 142 tons		£22 5 0½	at 5s	35 10 0
” caulkers labour			at 3s	21 6 0
” launching &[c]				5 0 0
” white oakham	0	2 14	at 32s 8d	1 0 5

[£]1754 19 6

Built for £15 per register ton 142 tons	2130 0 0
[profit]	£ 375 1 0

[next page] Amount brought up   £1754 19 6
Sawing not charged   50 0 0

[£]1804 19 6

[¹The use of smaller writing in the MS links Robert Drake with the £22 5s 0½. This craftsman is mentioned in an advertisement in *Trewman's Exeter Flying Post*, 22 March 1827, relating to 'two desirable family houses to be let' at Topsham – 'for further particulars apply to Mr Robert Drake, joiner'.]

An account of timber, plank &c &c used on a sloop of 76 tons register called the *Flower* which was built for Captn Richd Court Treatt of Exmouth and the exact quantity know[n] to be correct, Topsham, October 14th, 1819. Built at Topsham. [Signed] Danl B. Davy

Oak timber	Feet	inches		£	s	d
21 floors	175	1				
48 first foothooks	232	9				
91 second foothooks	341	9				
102 thirds & tops	228	0				
	977	7				
18 beams	180	1				
16 carlings	16	10				
38 ledges	22	0				
8 stem knight heads &c	80	3				
9 transoms &c	47	9				
19 stern timbers &c	72	7				
4 keelson &c	69	3				
– rudder	12	9				
41 chocks of different kinds	107	4				
19 certain pieces	104	2				
4 breasthooks	17	4				
52 knees	90	10				
31 stantions	59	0	= 1857 9 at 3s	278	13	3

	carried up					
	Feet	inches		£	s	d
To brought up	1857	9		278	13	3
,, elm timber	128	2	at 2s 6d	16	0	5

Oak plank	Feet	inches	solid feet			
4½ in. oak plank	60	10	= 22 9			
4 in. ditto	334	11	= 111 7			
3½ in. ditto	103	8	= 30 2			
3 in. ditto	359	11	= 87 6			
2½ in. ditto	492	9	= 102 6			
2 in. ditto	2952	9	= 492 10			
1½ in. ditto	221	4	= 27 7			
5 in. ditto	29	10	= 12 5 = 50/887 4 at £12	212	17	7

17 37

			solid			[£	s	d]
3½ in. elm plank	140	5	= 40	11				
2½ in. elm plank	663	10	= 138	3 =	50/179 2 at [£]7=	25	1	2
					3 29			
4 in. fir plank	54	6	= 18	2				
2½ in. ditto	552	7	= 115	1				
1½ in. ditto	126	11	= 15	10 =	50/149 1 at [£]12=	35	15	3
carried over					2 49	£568	7	8

			£	s	d
To brought over			568	7	8

	Feet	in.		£	s	d
,, 1½ in. deal used by joiners, cabin &c &c	13	0	at 9d	0	9	9
,, 1 in. ditto ditto	421	0	at 6d	10	10	0
,, ¾ in. ditto ditto	26	0	at 4½d	0	9	9
,, ½ in. ditto ditto	220	0	at 3d	2	15	0
,, ¼ in. ditto ditto	180	0	at 7½d	5	12	6
To treenails 4080			at 80s	16	6	3
,, ditto wedges 3500			at 5s		17	6
,, ditto puncheons 3000			at 5s		15	0
,, wedges 28 dozen			at 2s	2	16	0
,, oakham 5 Cwt 0 qrs 0 lbs			at 26s	6	10	0
,, tar 2 barrels			at 24s	2	8	0
,, pitch 3 [Cwt] 0 0			at 12s	1	16	0
,, nails				[blank]		

	Ton	cwt	qrs	lbs		£	s	d
,, iron fastenings exactly	1	3	1	19	at 13s 6d	51	6	0
,, shipwrights labour 75 tons					at 33s	123	15	0
,, joiners labour 75 tons					at 5s	19	0	0
,, caulkers labour 75 tons					at 3s	11	5	0
,, small nails used by joiners 2800					at 9[s]	1	5	0
						826	4	5

		£	s	d
Deduction of 30s per load charged on oak & deal plank £10 10s instead of £12		31	5	0
		794	19	5
Built for £10 10s per register ton	at £10 10s	787	15	0
	[loss]	7	4	5

[The *Flower* of Exeter was first registered at Exeter on 4 October 1819 (No 29); she was re-registered 1 March 1824 (No 63), Richard Court Treatt master. Her dimensions were: tonnage 76 ⁴⁷⁄₉₄; length 57 ft 11 in.; breadth 18 ft 4 in.; and depth in hold 9 ft 4 in. She was a square-sterned, carvel-built smack with one deck, one mast and a running bowsprit. Richard Court Treatt of Exmouth, mariner, and Daniel Bishop Davy of Topsham, shipbuilder, owned 48 of her 64 shares; William Rice of Fenchurch Street, London, flower factor, owned eight; and John Scovell and Henry Scovell of Toppings Wharf, Tooley Street, Southwark, wharfingers, the remaining eight shares. Gilbert Perriam was endorsed as her new master in London on 25 March 1825, Peter Russell in London on 20 November 1827 and Thomas Carter in London on 14 April 1829. The vessel's Exeter registration was cancelled at Weymouth on 16 June 1829 (Exeter Customs House Register of Shipping Vol. 3 1824–1825).]

Plate 1. The 600–ton East Indiaman *Caroline* (later the *Batavia*), built by Robert Davy at Glasshouse, Countess Wear, in 1802. Copy of painting photographed by courtesy of Topsham Museum.

Plate 2. Derelict lime-kilns (since demolished) at Glasshouse, Countess Wear, the site of Robert Davy's first shipyard. Photograph by C. N. Ponsford.

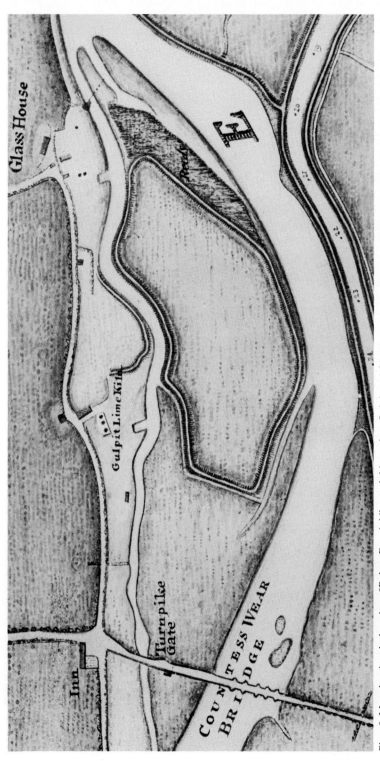

Plate 3. Map showing the location of Robert Davy's kilns and shipyards at Gulpit and Glasshouse, below Countess Wear Bridge. The Exeter Canal and river Exe are in the foreground. Detail from 'Plan of the Exeter Canal Navigation shewing the improvements proposed by James Green, civil engineer, 1819'. Devon Record Office, Exeter. Focus Photography, Exeter.

Plate 4. Triple portrait of the West Indiaman *Medina*, built at Topsham in 1811 by Robert Davy and part-owned by him. Oil painting by Thomas Whitcombe formerly in the Science Museum, London. Photograph by courtesy of the Science Museum.

Plate 5. The schooner *Post Boy* built by D. B. Davy at Topsham in 1831. Oil painting by W. J. Huggins. In 1854 the vessel was sold to Australian owners and was lost on a reef 11 years later. Photograph by courtesy of John Cole, Esq.

Plate 6. The schooner *Fanny Voase*, 133 tons, built at Hull in 1819 by Dikes, King and Co. She was employed in the Oporto wine trade and was possibly one of three such vessels mentioned by D. B. Davy as being under construction there that year. Oil painting by John Ward of Hull. Town Docks Museum, Hull, inv. no. M1. 46. 76.

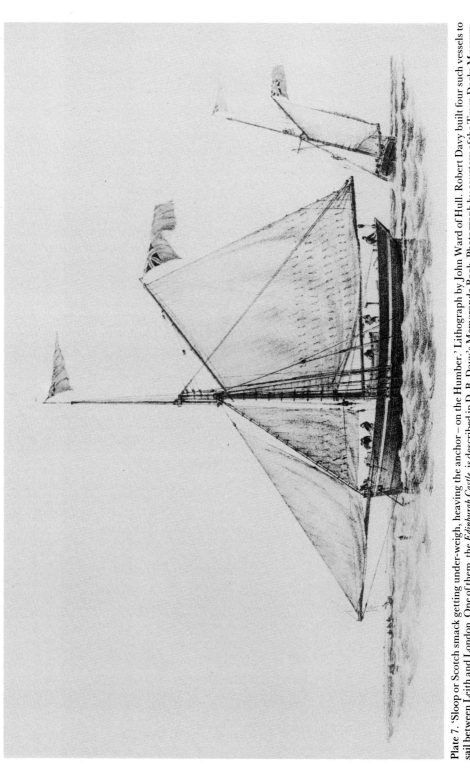

Plate 7. 'Sloop or Scotch smack getting under-weigh, heaving the anchor – on the Humber.' Lithograph by John Ward of Hull. Robert Davy built four such vessels to sail between Leith and London. One of them, the *Edinburgh Castle*, is described in D. B. Davy's Memoranda Book. Photograph by courtesy of the Town Docks Museum, Hull.

Plate 8. A sloop or 'stone boat' on the river Exe at Topsham, c. 1900. Robert Davy operated a small fleet of such vessels to bring stone from the Torbay area to his lime-kilns. Photograph by courtesy of Topsham Museum.

Plate 9. A cargo of limestone, awaiting collection at low tide in the river Exe near the old Davy kilns at Higher Wear, above Countess Wear Bridge. Postcard bearing 1904 postmark.

Plate 10. The schooner *Ebenezer*, built by Daniel Bishop Davy in 1828 and pictured here at Malta under the command of Captain John Holman of Topsham. Her original building contract is set out as Appendix D. Photograph by courtesy of Topsham Museum.

An account of timber, plank &c &c used on a sloop of 91 tons register called the *Fortitude* built for Capt. Thos Holman & Company, the exact quantity of all the materials used know[n] to be correct.
February 29th, 1820, Topsham. [Signed] Danl B. Davy

Oak timber	Feet	inches			
23 floors	225	7			
68 first foothooks	384	3			
61 second foothooks	245	10			
152 thirds, tops &c &c	403	5			
	1259	1			
23 beams	207	1			
34 carlings	65	6			
34 ledges	38	2			
Certain pieces	187	2			
Knight heads &c	39	8			
Transoms	35	3			
Breasthooks	27	2			
Keelson & deadwood	74	5			
Rudder	31	0			
Stern timbers	36	4			
Stantions	78	5			
Chocks	84	9			
Knees	137	2	= 2301 2 at 3s		£345 3s 0d

				Feet	inches	£	s	d
To brought over				2301	2	345	3	0
	Feet	inches	solid					
5 inch oak plank	29	11	= 12	6				
4½ ditto	90	6	= 33	11				
4 ditto	373	10	= 124	7				
3½ ditto	38	5	= 11	2				
3 ditto	584	8	= 146	11				
2¾ ditto	65	3	= 14	10				
2½ ditto	1317	4	= 274	4				
2 ditto	3140	4	= 523	4				
1½ ditto	332	4	= 41	6				
		50/1183	1= 23 33	at £11	260	5	9	

Elm plank	Feet	inches	solid				
3½ inch elm	158	10	= 46	4			
2½ ditto	622	3	= 129	7			
		50/175 11	= 3 25	at £7	24	10	0

[cont'd]

Fir plank	Feet	inches		solid	
4 inch fir	67	3	=	22	5
2½ ditto	704	9	=	146	9
1½ ditto	91	10	=	11	5
1 ditto	104	10	=	8	8

50/189 3 = 3 39   at £11   43 15 7

140 feet of elm timber   at 2s   14   0   0

                                                  687 14 4

					£	s	d
To brought up					687	14	4
	Feet		d[pence]				
1½ inch board for the joiners	56	at	7½	1 15 0			
1¼ ditto ditto	357	at	6¼	9 5 11			
1 ditto ditto	272	at	5	5 13 4			
⅞ ditto ditto	310	at	4¾	6 2 8			
¾ ditto ditto	90	at	3¾	1 8 1½			
½ ditto ditto	558	at	2½	5 16 3			
Edging for sundry purposes	98	at	2	0 16 4			
Joiners labour 91 tons		at	5s 6d	25 0 0	55	17	7½
7450 treenails		at	80s	25 16 0			
5000 ditto wedges		at	5s	1 5 0			
27 dozen elm wedges		at	5s	6 15 0			
5 [cwt] 0 0 of oakham		at	26s	6 10 0			
½ cwt of white ditto		at	32s 8d	0 16 4			
2 barrels of tar				2 8 0			
3[cwt] 0 0 of pitch		at	12s	1 16 0			
6300 small nails		at	9s	2 16 6			
5 cwt of deck spikes		at	26s	6 10 0			
5 cwt of ribbin nails		at	26s	6 10 0			
Iron fastenings 31Cwt 0qrs 0lbs		at	42s	65 2 0			
Caulkers labour		at	3s	13 13 0			
Shipwrights labour		at	30s	136 10 0			
Sawyers labour 34,670		at	3s	52 12 0	= 328	19	10

                                                  1072 11 9½

Deduct for sawin[g]   £12 12s 0d

Built for £10 10s per register ton   955 10 0

                          [loss]   117   1 9½

[The *Fortitude* of Exeter, John Holman master, had one mast and was sloop rigged with a running bowsprit when re-registered at Exeter on 8 January 1824 (No 4). She was then altered into a two-masted schooner and was registered anew on 14 March 1824 (No 74); she was carvel built with a square stern and one deck. Her principal dimensions were: length 63 ft 9 in.; breadth below the main wales 18 ft 10 in.; depth in the hold 10 ft 4 in.; and tonnage 91 ⁹⁄₉₄ (Exeter Customs House Register of Shipping Vol. 3 1824–1825).]

An account of timber, plank &c &c used on a lighter of 83 tons register called the *Majestic* built of [for] Mr Wm Ash Junr of Starcross. Built in the year 1820 at Topsham.

At £5 per ton £415 [Signed] D. B. Davy

	Feet	ins	sawing		£	s	d
Floors	198	6	= 1931				
1st futtocks	323	8	= 3058				
2nd & 3rd ditto	288	9	= 3102				
Certain pieces, ledges, carlings, knees, stem beams &c &c &c	420	0	= 3825				
			11,916 at 3s per 100 feet		17	17	6

	Feet	ins			£	s	d
Oak timber	1230	11	at	2s 6d per foot	153	17	4
			sawing	sol[i]d			
5¼ ins oak plank	89	7	104	39 1			
4 ins ditto	65	5	83	21 9			
3½ ,, ,,	231	9	232	67 6			
3 ,, ,, [?161]	166	11	148	41 8			
2½ ,, ,,	832	3	538	173 4			
2 ,, ,,	2156	6	1291	359 5			
1½ ,, ,,	218	1	127	27 3			
			2,523	at 3s per 100 feet	3	15	6
			50/730 0				

			£	s	d
Loads of oak plank	14 30 at £10		147	10	0
			323	0	4

					£	s	d
Brought up					323	0	4
	Feet	ins	sawing	solid			
3 ins fir plank	97	9	345	24 5			
2 ,, ditto	525	0	818	87 6			
1½ ,, ,,	216	1	328	27 0			
			1,491 at 3s per 100 feet		2	4	9
	838	10	50/138 11				
			at £7 2 28 11		19	3	0
3 ins elm plank	77	6	45	19 4			
2½ ins ditto	151	3	80	31 6			
2 ins ditto	786	0	35 6	131 2			
			481 at 3s per 100 feet			14	4
	[1014]	9	50/182 0				
			3 32 [at] £10		37	12	0

[cont'd]

	[Cwt	qrs	lbs]		£	s	d
Pitch	3	1	14	at 14s	2	7	3
Oakham	3	3	0	at 26s	4	17	0
Treenails	3500			at 70s per m	11	5	0
Wedges & puncheons	5831			at 4s per m	1	1	9
Set wedges	17 dozen			at 2s 6d per dozen	2	2	6
Tar 1 barrel					1	5	0
Nails	2	2	8	at 27s	3	9	6
1100 small nails					0	10	0
Joiners labour & materials					17	0	0
Iron fastenings					15	0	0
Caulkers labour			83 tons at 3s		12	9	0
Shipwrights labour			83 tons at 25s per ton		107	5	0
					561	6	5

Built at £5 per ton   83½ [tons]   £417 10 0
                                   Loss 143 16 5
                                        £561 6 5

An account of timber, plank &c used on a sloop called the *Good Intent* built for Captn Wm Pearse of Topsham. Built in 1820 – 76 tons register at £10 10s.

	solid		sawing		£	s	d
	[Feet	inches]	[Feet]				
Floors	146	0	1154				
First futtocks	429	8	3798				
Second ditto	181	11	1901				
Third ditto	333	0	3678				
Knees	121	3	1634				
Carlings	48	2	653				
Beams	172	2	1412				
Stantions	42	8	529				
Stem &c	61	3	376				
Deadwood, post &c	114	9	742				
Keelson	46	4	269				
Stern timbers &c	71	8	624				
Gripe, harpins &c	19	4	212				
Breast hooks	20	3	184				
Sundry pieces	119	5	1109				
			18,275 = 3s				
			[per 100 feet]		27	8	3
	1927	10	at 2s 6d		240	19	7
Elm timber	139	4	at 2s	849 3s	13	18	8
					1	5	6
Fir timber	9	2		68 at 3s	1	7	6
					0	2	0
	carried forward				£285	1	6

[cont'd]
Brought forward [to next page]   £285 1 6

			solid				
5 ins oak plank	56	2	23	5	77		
4½ ins "	32	5	12	1	57		
4 ins "	244	2	81	4	283		
3½ ins "	274	0	79	11	298		
3 ins "	535	0	133	9	420		
2½ ins "	1864	11	388	6	1243		
2 ins "	1577	2	263	1	1035		
1½ ins "	197	4	24	7	129		
		50/1006	8		3542 at 3s		5 6 3
			20	6	at £10		201 4 0
2½ ins fir plank	764	2	158	4	663		
2 ins "	33	6	5	7	26		
1½ ins "	112	3	14	0	47		
1 ins "	100	8	8	4	32		
		50/186	3		768 at 3s		1 3 0
			3	3 6	at [£]10		30 12 0
3 ins elm plank	161	9	40	5	120		
2½ ins "	609	3	126	10	372		
		50/167	3		492 at 3s		0 14 8
			3	17	at £7		23 8 0

		£ s d
Joiners labour and materials at per ton	10s	38 0 0
Shipwrights labour	30s	114 0 0
Caulkers labour	3s	11 8 0
Fastening iron		40 0 0
carried forward		£750 17 5

		£ s d
Brought forward [to next page]		£750 17 5
To 3500 treenails	at 80s	14 0 0
" 4[cwt] 2[qrs] 0[lbs] of oakham		5 17 0
" 1[qr] 14[lbs] of white ditto	[at] 36s	0 12 3
" 3000 of treenail wedges	[at] 5s	0 15 0
" 3000 of puncheons	[at] 4s	0 12 0
" 5[cwt] 0[qrs] 0[lbs] of spike nails	[at] 24s	6 0 0
" tar two barrels	[at] 24s	2 8 0
" pitch 3[cwt] 0[qrs] 0[lbs]	[at] 12s	1 16 0
		[£]782 17 8

Built at £10 10s per ton 76 tons   £798

An account of timber, plank &c &c used on a schooner called the *Britannia* built for Mr John Parker of Exmouth. Built in the year 1822 at Topsham for £10 10s per register tons [sic] = 90½ tons register.

['sawing' added in another hand]

	[Cubic Feet ins]		[Foot run]
20 floors	248	11	1650
First foothooks	316	1	2446
Second ditto	120	10	1496
Third ditto	322	9	3567
Knees &c	83	1	1110
Beams	235	7	1581
Carlings & ledges	48	0	395
Sundry pieces from Hills field used	501	0	2694
Certain pieces	440	7	3074

18,013 at 3s per 1000ft   2 14 6
[see end of account]

Oak timber   2316 10   solid at 2s 6d [per cubic foot] 289 12 1

	[Sq. ft ins]		[Cu. ft ins]		[foot run sawing?]	
6½ ins oak plank	7	0	3	9	20	
6 ” „	5	0	2	6	16	
5 ” „	39	7	16	6	63	
4 ” „	583	3	194	5	796	
3½ ” „	27	4	7	11	40	
3 ” „	290	6	72	7	245	
2½ ” „	1113	4	231	11	690	
2¼ ” „	33	11	6	4	16	
2 ” „	3120	6	520	1	1823	
1½ ” „	215	11	27	0	145	218 2 0
			1083	0	3854 at 3s	5 15 8

Loads of oak plank =   21   33   at £10   516 4 3

Brought forward   £516 4 3

	[Sq. ft ins]		solid			
Elm timber	146	1	[Cu. ft ins]		at 2s 3d	16 8 8
Elm sawing					1125 [foot run]	
3 ins elm plank	172	11	43	3	122	
2½ ins ,,	837	2	174	6	483	
2 ins ,,	51	0	8	6	46	
	50/226	3			2876 at 3s	4 6 2

[per 100 foot]

4 26   at £7   31 13 0

[cont'd]

Fir timber	8	7			at 3s		1 5 8
4 inch fir plank	13	0	4	4	31		
2½ ins ,, ,,	777	10	162	0	699		
1½ ins ,, ,,	77	4	9	7	44		
1 ins ,, ,,	71	4	6	0	25		37 14 0

50/181 11   699 at 3s   1 0 11

3   31

	[Cwt	qrs	lbs]			
Pitch	1	2	7	[at] 12s		0 18 8
Oakham	4	2	19	[at] 26s		6 1 5
Treenails 5281				at 70s		13 2 6
Wedges 18 dozen				at 2s 6d		2 5 0
Tar 2 barrels						2 8 0
Puncheerns [puncheons] 3000						0 12 0
Nails	5	0	0			6 0 0
Wedges 3000						0 15 0
Iron fastenings						40 0 0

carried forward   £680 15 3

Brought forward   £680 15 3
Shipwrights labour 90 tons   at 30s   135 0 0
Joiners labour, materials &c   45
Caulkers labour 90 tons   [at]3s   13 10 0

£874 5 3

Mistake in oak sawing on the frame timbers   24 6 0

898 11 3

Built at £10 10s per ton   90½   £950 5s 0d

[When the *Britannia* of Exmouth was re-registered at Exeter on 16 February 1824 it was stated that John Parker of Exmouth, merchant, was ill and incapable of attending. He was the owner of 32 of her 64 shares; the other 32 were owned by her master, John Parker the younger. The *Britannia* was schooner rigged with two masts and a running bowsprit; she was carvel built and had a square stern and one deck. Her principal dimensions were; length 62 ft 4 in.; breadth 19 ft 0¾ in.; depth in the hold 10 ft 6½ in.; and burden 90 ³⁰/₉₄ tons (Exeter Customs House Register of Shipping Vol. 3 1824–1825, No 34 – 1824).]

An account of timber, plank &c used on a lighter called the *Neptune* built for Ben Follett & Co. of Topsham in 1823 – 57 tons register at £5 per ton.

	[Feet ins]	[Solid]	[Sawing, in feet]
Floors	85 0		506
First futtocks	135 8		1211
Second and third ditto	238 3		2300
Sundry pieces	101 0		707
Chocks	4 4		162

[cont'd]	[Feet ins]	[Solid]	[Sawing, in feet]			
Beams	44 8		437			
Breast hooks &c	8 3		76			
Knees	36 11		610			
Ledges & carlings	19 8		349			
			6358 at 3s	9	10	5
	663 9	at 2s 6d		82	19	4
4 ins oak plank	3 7	1 2	6			
3½ ins ,, ,,	5 9	1 7	12			
3 ins ,, ,,	201 7	50 4	164			
2½ [ins] ,, ,,	216 8	45 1	144			
2 [ins] ,, ,,	1787 9	297 7	1149			
1½ [ins] ,, ,,	341 5	42 8	220			
		50/438 5	1695 at 3s	2	10	9
		8 38	at £10	87	12	0
Elm timber	61 4	at 2s		6	2	9
carried forward				£188	15	3

	[Feet ins]	solid	[Sawing, in feet]			
Brought forward				£188	15	0
3 ins elm plank	16 10	4 2	66			
2½ ins	127 7	26 6	140			
2 ins	809 4	134 11	439			
		50/165 7	645 at 3s	0	19	3
		3 15	at £7	23	2	0
2 ins fir plank	423 6	66 8	293			
1 ins ditto	11 8	1 0				
¾ ins ditto	349 2	24 0	295			
		50/ 91 8	588 at 3s	0	17	7
		1 41	at £10	13	4	0

	[Cwt qrs lbs]					
Nails	2 0 2	at 30s		3	0	4
Wedges 17 dozen		[at] 2s 6d		2	2	6
Treenails 2676		at 70s		9	3	0
Oakham	2 2 26	at 26s		3	11	0
Pitch	1 2 0	at 12s		0	18	0
½ barrel tar				0	15	0
Puncheons 2700				0	7	0
Furze 24 bundles				0	5	0
20 lbs tallow				0	10	0
1800 nails at 7d				0	10	6
Caulkers labour	57 tons	at 2s 6d		7	2	6
Shipwrights labour	57 tons	at 25s		71	5	0
Joiners labour		at 5s		14	5	0
Brought forward				£340	10	8

[cont'd]

Brought forward		£340 10 8
Iron fastenings		15 0 0
		355 10 8

Built at £5 per ton 57 tons   £285

Loss   = 70 10 8

[£]355 10 8

An account of oak timber, plank &c used in building a schooner of 92 $^{63}/_{94}$ tons register. Built at Topsham for the London trade, Capt. Thos Popham, June 1st 1824, at £10 per ton register, called the *Swift*.

	[Feet inches]	sawing		[£ s d]
Floors	288 11	1887		
First futtocks	379 2	3220		
Second ditto	234 4	2329		
Third & tops	380 10	4577		
Knees	131 11	1941		
Beams	177 1	1332		
Ledges & carlings	31 0	506		
Sundry certain pieces	372 10	2870		
		18,662 at 3s		27 19 10
	1996 1	at 2s 8d		266 2 10½
5 ins oak plank	23 4	9 8	28	
4½ ins ,,	24 10	9 3	24	
4 ins ,,	440 9	156 11	545	
3½ ins ,,	184 1	53 8	238	
3 ins ,,	685 5	171 4	499	
2½ ins ,,	1680 2	350 0	1193	
2 ins ,,	1818 9	303 1	1283	
1½ ins ,,	169 9	20 11	115	
			3925 at 3s	5 17 9
		50/1074 10		
		21 24	at £10	215 0 0
		carried up		£515 0 5½

Brought forward				£515 0 5½
Elm timber	137 6 at 2s			13 15 0
Elm sawing		981 at 3s		1 9 5
3 ins elm plank	213 4	53 4	178	
2½ ins	726 9	150 4	491	
		/203 8	669 at 3s	1 0 0
		5 3 8 at £7		35 8 6
Fir timber	7 1 at 3s			1 1 3
Ditto sawing		54 at 3s		0 1 7

[cont'd]

2½ ins fir plank	673	1	140	2	655 at 3s			
2 ins	44	2	7	4	27			
1½ ins	88	8	11	1	37			
1 ins	72	5	6	0	29			
1¼ ins	84	11	8	9				
Sawing on chocks &c					1381 at 3s			
			50/173	4	2129	3	3	7
					3 23 at £10	35	0	0
7 ins fir fir [sic] for bulwarks &c	275				at 4d	4	11	8
5700 tree nails					at 70s	20	2	6
1110 ditto wedges					at 5s	0	5	8
28½ dozen wedges					at 2s 6d	3	11	3
Oil						0	7	6
Small coals	8	5			at 10s	4	6	3
Greese	60 lbs					0	10	0
			carried forward			£639	14	7½

	Brought forward					£639	14s	7½d
		[Cwt	qrs	lbs]				
Black oakum		6	1	0	at 26s	8	2	6
White [oakum]		0	0	12	at 30s	0	3	2½
Pitch		4	3	18	at 12s	2	19	0
Rosin		0	2	4	at 12s	0	6	6
Nails		4	1	20	at 25s	5	10	9
Lamblack [lampblack]			1			0	0	10
Coal tar		10 gallons				0	5	0
Small nails 1200						0	12	0
New boat						8	8	–
Oars &c						2	2	0
Iron fastenings						40	14	10
Joiners labour					at 5s 6d	25	6	0
Caulkers labour					at 3s	13	16	0
Shipwrights labour					at 30s	138	0	0
						[£]886	1	5

92¾ [tons]

[x £] 10

£927 10 0   [Profit   £41 8s 9d]

[The *Swift* of Exeter, Thomas Popham master, was first registered at Exeter on 21 May 1824. She was carvel built with a square stern and had one deck and two masts. Her principal dimensions were: length 62 ft 6 in.; breadth 18 ft 11¾ in.; and depth in the hold 10 ft. She was schooner rigged with a running bowsprit and her tonnage was recorded as 92 63/94, the same as that given by Daniel Bishop Davy. Captain Popham owned 32 of her 64 shares; Davy owned eight shares and there were four other owners. Charles Edwards was endorsed as her new master at Exeter on 4 July 1827 (Exeter Customs House Register of Shipping Vol. 3, 1824–1825, No 89 – 1824).]

[Loose paper giving the sizes of materials used in a small vessel]

Beams 7 ins sided, 7 [ins] moulded
Floors, English oak, 8 sided, 9 at cutting down
Deck plank 2½ inch thick – copper nailed
Plank sheer 2¾ ins thick
Rails, fir, 2½ ins thick, 5 ins wide
Bottom plank, oak, 2½ ins thick
Bottom plank, elm, 2½ ins thick
Bilges, elm, 3½ ins thick
Wales, oak, three strakes 4[-] ins, 6½ ins wide
Black strake, oak, 3 ins thick
Hold beams 8 ins sided, 7 ins moulded
Two thick strakes of 3 ins on the floor heads inside
A 3 ins oak plank on the first futtock heels
A stringer under the deck beams 10 ins wide & 11 ins thick, the beams
    bolted through the stringer & dove tailed in the stringer 1½ ins
Keelson sided 10½ ins & moulded 11½ ins
Copper fastened under the wales
Paint strake 3 ins thick, 9 ins wide
Black strakes 3 ins thick, 8 ins wide
Topside strake 2¼ [ins] thick, 6½ ins wide
An iron hanging knee under each deck beam – the wash strake inside to be
    reeded with 5 or 6 small reeds
Height of the upper part of the rail from the deck 2 ft 7 ins
Floors fastened with ⅞ ins copper bolts
Keelson fastened with 1 ins copper bolts
Butt bolts – with ½ ins copper bolts
Thick plank on bilges with ⅝ ins copper bolts
1st futtocks sided at heel 7¾ [ins] at head [–]
2nd futtocks sided at heel [–] at head [–]
3rd & tops sided at heel [–] at head [–]
[The dimension of the floors and first futtocks suggest that she was a vessel of about 80 tons, a small schooner, perhaps like the *Eliza*.]

DETAILED DIMENSIONS RELATING TO SHIPS' PLANS OR 'DRAFTS'

[The frames or sections from the dead-flat or midship bend [⊠] to the bow are distinguished by letters of the alphabet, and those from ⊠ to the stern by figures.

Key to abbreviations used by D. B. Davy

F G	floor guide	2 S	Second foothook sirmark
F S	floor sirmark	2 H	second foothook head
F H	floor head	3 S	third foothook sirmark
1 S	first foothook sirmark	M B	main breadth
1 H	first foothook head	T B	top breadth

For an explanation of these and other shipbuilding terms see Introduction and Glossary.]

Dimensions of the sloop called the *Bee* built by Mr [Robert] Davy in 1815 for the E[dinburgh], G[lasgow] & Leith Shipping Company, Scotland, which answered & sailed very well.

[The number '0' in the feet column is used by Davy in most instances to represent 'ditto', that is the number immediately above.]

Fore body square timbers

On guide	Ft	in. pt	F S		F H		1 S		1 H	
⊠	3	7¾	6	3½	7	8	8	5½	8	11
A	3	7	0	2½	0	7	0	4¾	0	10⅜
B	0	6¼	0	1	0	5¼	0	3¼	0	9½
C	0	5	5	10	0	2½	0	0¾	0	8¼
D	0	2¼	0	6	6	9¾	7	8¼	0	5¼
E	2	11	5	0	0	2½	0	1½	0	1
F	0	5½	4	3½	5	5½	6	4½	7	5½
G	1	9¾	3	5	4	6	5	4¼	6	6¾
H	0	10	2	3¼	3	3	4	0¼	5	4

Breadth at

	Lower harpin		top breadth	
⊠	7	10½	7	7¼
A	0	10	0	7
B	0	9½	0	6⅝
C	0	8¼	0	6⅜
D	0	6¾	0	5¼
E	0	4	0	3½
F	6	10½	0	1
G	0	1¾	6	8½
H	4	1¾	4	11

D. Davy

On guide	Ft	[ins.]	After body square timbers F S		F H		1 S		1 H	
1	3	7½	6	3	7	5¼	8	7½	8	10
2	3	6½	6	2	0	4¾	0	6	8	9⅜
3	0	5½	6	0	0	3¾	0	1	0	8¼
4	0	4¼	5	9	0	0½	7	10	0	7
5	0	2½	0	5	6	8¼	0	6¼	0	2¾
6	3	0	0	1	0	3½	0	2¼	7	11¼
7	2	9	4	8	5	10	6	9¼	0	8
8	2	5½	0	2	0	3½	0	3½	0	3½
9	0	1	3	5½	4	9	5	9¼	6	10¼
10	1	7¾	3	0	0	0¾	0	1¼	0	3½
11	1	2	2	3½	3	3½	4	4½		
12	0	8¾	1	6½	2	5½	3	5½	5	7½
13	0	3	0	8½	1	5	2	5¼	4	9

Breadths at

Lower harpin	Ft	in	Top breadth	Ft	in
1	7	9½	2	7	6
2	0	9	3	0	5½
3	0	8¼	4	0	4¼
4	0	7¼	5	0	2⅜
5	0	6	6	0	1
6	0	4¾	7	6	11
7	0	3¼	8	0	9½
8	0	1¼	9	0	7½
9	6	11¾	10	0	5
10	0	9	11	0	2¼
11	0	7	12	6	0
12	0	4	13	5	9
13	0	1	—	—	—

[The main dimensions of the sloop *Bee*, 53 tons, were: length 47 ft; breadth 16 ft 5 in.; and depth of hold 8 ft (Hedderwick: *A Treatise on Marine Architecture*, p. 147).]

Dimensions of the brig call'd the *Sedulous* (No 9) of about 130 tons register built by Robt Davy on speculation in 1817 and composed by Danl B. Davy & likewise laid down by him; built at Gulpit by Mr Bishop at per ton 30s [for shipwrights' labour] as a taker.

	Feet	in.
Length for admeasurement	72	2
Breadth for admeasurement	20	10½
Depth in the hold	13	6

& admeasures

No [sic] 134 9/94 tons

No 9			Ft	in.
Length from fore perpendicular to timber N			4	1¾
Ditto from No [? N] to ⊠ 27 ft 0 in. Room & space			1	9¾

Keel up & down 12 inches, across 11 inches midships, ends 9½ inches
Stem thwartships 10 inches
Ditto fore & aft at the wales 10½ inches and all up and down 10½

Square body Guide			Floor sirm[ar]k			Floor head		
M	1	9	N	1	9	N	2	6
L	2	9½	M	3	5¼	M	4	5
I	4	0½	L	4	8¼	L	5	9¼
G	4	8½	I	6	4	I	7	5
E	5	1	G	7	4¼	G	8	6½
C	5	2	E	7	11¼	E	9	2
A	5	3¼	C	8	2½	C	9	5¼
⊠	5	3¼	A	8	3¾	A	9	7
			⊠	8	3¾	⊠	9	7½

1 S	Ft	inches	2 S			M B		
N	4	0	N	6	2½	N	6	1
M	6	0¾	M	8	1	M	7	7¾
L	7	5	L	9	5¼	L	8	7
I	9	3	I	11	1	I	9	7½
G	10	3	G	11	10	G	9	10
E	10	10⅜	E	12	0¾	E	10	0½
C	11	1	C	12	2	C	10	0½
A	11	2	A	12	3⅝	A	10	0½
⊠	11	3	⊠	12	4	⊠	10	0½

1 H	Ft	in.	2 H	Ft	in.	T B		
N	5	4	N	7	0	N	6	7
M	7	3½	M	8	8¼	M	7	11
L	8	8¾	L	9	11½	L	8	7
I	10	6	I	11	4	I	9	3¼
G	11	5	G	11	11⅞	G	9	6½
E	11	10⅛	E	12	2	E	9	7¾
C	12	0	C	12	2¼	C	9	7¾
A	12	1½	A	12	2¾	A	9	7¾
⊠	12	2	⊠	12	3	⊠		

Breadth of body moulded 20 ft 1 in., extreme 20 [ft] 6 [in.]

Guide up on the rabbet from the upper rabbet of keel 3 ft 5 in., F S [floor sirmark] 5 [ft] 11 [in.], F H [floor head] 7 [ft] 11 [in.], out from the stem 7½ [in.?] each.
Up on middle line in body plan the Sirm[ar]ks
Guide up on middle line 3 [ft] 11½ [in.], on base 4 [ft] 2½ [in.].
F S up on middle line 6 [ft] 3 [in.] = on base ditto 7 [ft] 1¾ [in.]

F H out on base 9 [ft] 1 [in.] = on middle ditto 7 [ft] 5 [in.] =
1 S on middle line 9 [ft] 10 [in.] = on side line 1 [ft] 10⅝ [in.]
1 H on side 4 [ft] 4¾ [in.], on middle 12 [ft] 0 [in.] =
2 S on side 8 [ft] 8¾ [in.], on middle 13 [ft] 10½ [in.] =
2 H on side 8 [ft] 8 [in.], on middle 15 [ft] 8 [in.] =
Water lines, 5 in number, each 2 feet apart, No 6 ditto = 11 ft 7 in., No 7
water line 13 ft 7 in., No 8 ditto 15 ft 7½ in.
Stem up on square timber (I) from upper rabbet 1 inch, on L 1 ft 0 in., on M
2 [ft] 1½ [in.], on N 4 [ft] 0 [in.]
Perpendicular from square timber No [? N] 4 ft 1¾ in.
Lower rabbet of stem from perpendicular 10 [ft] 11 [in.], upper ditto 12 [ft]
5 [in.]. 1st water line from perpendicular 6 [ft] 2¼ [in.], 2nd ditto 4 [ft] 3
[in.], 3rd ditto 3 [ft] 2 [in.], 4th ditto 2 [ft] 6 [in.], 5 [th] ditto 2 [ft] 1½ [in.],
6 [th] ditto 1 [ft] 10 [in.], 7 [th] ditto 1 [ft] 6 [in.], 8 [th] ditto 1 [ft] 3½ [in.]

After body square timbers

Guide			F head			1 head		
⊗	5	3¼	⊗	9	7	⊗	–	
1	5	2¼	1	9	5	1	12	0½
3	5	1	3	9	2	3	11	10
5	4	11	5	8	11	5	11	7
7	4	7½	7	8	5½	7	11	3½
9	4	2	9	7	11	9	10	11½
11	3	3½	11	6	0	11	8	11
13	2	8	13	5	1	13	7	11¾
15	1	11½	15	3	8½	15	6	7½
16	1	6¼	16	2	11	16	5	8¾
17	1	0¾	17	2	1	17	4	7
18	0	6	18	1	1	18	3	2½

F sirm[ar]k			1 sirm[ar]k			2 sirm[ar]k		
⊗	8	3¼	⊗	11	7½	⊗	[-]	[-]
1	8	1	1	11	2	1	12	2½
3	8	0	3	11	0	3	12	0
5	7	9	5	10	8	5	11	11
7	7	3⅜	7	10	2⅜	7	11	8½
9	6	8¾	9	9	8½	9	11	4
11	5	1⅜	11	7	8	11	9	6
13	4	3	13	6	7	13	8	10
15	3	1	15	5	1	15	7	10
16	2	5	16	4	2	16	7	2
17	1	8½	17	3	0½	17	6	3
18	0	10	18	1	10½	18	4	11

2 H			T B			M B		
⊗	–	–	⊗	9	6½	⊗	10	0½
1	12	1¾	1	9	6	1	9	11¾
3	12	1	3	9	5	3	9	10¾
5	11	11½	5	9	3	5	9	9
7	11	10¼	7	9	2	7	9	8¾
9	11	7	9	9	0½	9	9	6½
11	9	10	11	7	9½	11	8	2
13	9	5½	13	7	7½	13	8	0
15	8	10¼	15	7	5	15	7	10
16	8	5¼	16	7	3½	16	7	8½
17	7	9	17	7	2½	17	7	6½
18	6	10	18	7	0	18	7	5

Height of M & TB [main and top breadth] in sheer plan

Fore body			Height of ditto in after body		
MB	Ft	in.	MB	[Ft	in.]
On stem	14	1¾	1	11	2
N	13	3	3	11	4
M	12	11	5	11	6½
L	12	6	7	11	8¾
I	11	10	9	11	10¾
G	11	5½	11	–	–
E	11	2	13	–	–
A	11	0	15	–	–
⊗	11	0	16	–	–
			17	–	–
TB	Ft	in.	18	–	–
On stem	15	11¾	19	–	–
N	15	7	20	–	–
M	15	4			
L	15	2	TB		
I	14	11¼	1	14	8
G	14	9	3	14	9
E	14	7½	5	14	10
A	14	6	7	15	0
⊗	14	6	9	15	3
			11	–	–
			13	–	–
			15	–	–
			16	–	–
			17	–	–
			18	–	–
			19	–	–
			20	–	–

Height of wales: lower edge

Stem	11	1¼	9	–
N	10	9¼	11	–
L	10	5	13	–
I	10	2	15	–
G	10	0	16	–
E	9	10⅛	17	–
C	9	9	18	–
A	9	8½		
⊠	9	8½		
(1)	9	9		
1	9	10		
3	9	11		
5	10	0½		
7	10	2½		

carried up

Draft No 10

Dimensions of 2 vessels as laid down by D. B. Davy called the *Mary* & *Dorothea*. The[y] sailed well and carried large cargoes.

		Ft	ins
Length from fore perpendicular to timber O	=	4	6½
Length from O to fore part of ⊠		30	1½
Brea[d]th of ⊠ timber		0	11
Length from the after part of ⊠ to timber 22		45	0
Length from timber 22 to after part of the stern post		1	0
		81	7

	Ft	ins
Breadth moulded	23	6
Room & space	1	10½
Height of main stem	21	9
Height of wing transom	14	0

Body plan	Ft	ins		Ft	ins
Guide up on middle line	4	9	Guide cut on baseline	5	4½
Floor sirmark	6	5	Floor sirmark	8	3¾
Floor head	7	9½	Floor head	10	8
1 sirm[ar]k	9	10	1 sirm[ar]k on side	2	3¾
1 head	12	0	1 head	4	10¾
2 sirmark	14	0	2 sirm[ar]k	8	5
2 head	16	0½	2 head	9	8
3 sirm[ar]k	17	11	3 sirm[ar]k	11	11½
			M B	13	10
Under part of main stem			T B	16	9
up on perpendicular	21	3			
Up on 0	3	8¾			
Ditto [on] N	1	9¼			
Ditto [on] M	0	6			

			Water lines up from baseline on keel		
From perpendicular on keel line	9	4			Ft [ins]
From perpendicular on 1 water line	5	7	No 1	2	0
Ditto	on 2 » 3	9	2	4	0
Ditto	on 3 » 2	7½	3	6	0
Ditto	on 4 » 1	11	4	8	0
Ditto	on 5 » 1	6	5	10	0
Ditto	on 6 » 0	11	6	12	0
Ditto	on 7 » 0	7	7	14	0
Ditto	on 8 » 0	2½	8	16	0

under part of rabit [rabbet] from these spots – 9 ins square further in
Rabit [rabbet] 3 ins further in on a square

Fore body plan

Guide			F G			F H		
⊠	6	6	⊠	9	0¾	⊠	10	8
(A)			D	8	8	D	10	2
(B)			F	8	2	F	9	9
A			H	7	4¾	H	9	0
B			K	6	3¼	K	7	7
D	6	2½	M	4	3	M	5	4½
F	5	11	N	2	9¾	N	3	11
H	5	4½	O	0	9½	O	1	10
K	4	7						
M	2	9						
N	1	4½						
O	–	–						

1 S			1 H			2 S		
⊠	12	4½	⊠	13	1	⊠	13	3
D	11	10¾	D	12	10	D	13	2
F	11	5	F	12	6	F	13	0
H	10	8	H	11	10	H	12	5
K	9	4	K	9	8	K	11	4½
M	7	1	M	8	8	M	9	9
N	5	7	N	7	2	N	8	5
O	3	5	O	5	11	O	6	2

2 H			3 S			M Breadth		
⊠	13	3½	⊠	13	2	⊠	11	9
D	13	3	D	13	2	B	11	9
F	13	1½	F	13	0	D	11	8¼
H	12	8½	H	12	9	F	11	7½
K	11	10½	K	11	11½	H	11	5
M	10	4¾	M	10	8	K	10	10
N	9	3	N	9	7½	M	9	9
O	7	2	O	7	7¾	N	8	8½
						O	7	0

T Breadth			M B Height			T B Height		
⊠	11	3	⊠	13	10	⊠	16	8
B	11	3	(B)	13	11½	(B)	16	10½
D	11	3	B	14	2	B	17	0
F	11	2½	D	14	5	D	17	2
H	11	2	F	14	8½	F	17	6
K	10	9½	H	15	1	H	17	9¼
M	9	10	K	15	7	K	18	1¾
N	8	11¾	M	16	1	M	18	6¾
O	7	7	N	16	4¾	N	18	9½
			O	16	8¼	O	19	1
			Stem 17		6	Stem 19		6½

After Body

Guide			F S			F H		
(2)	6	6	(2)	9	0¾	(2)	10	8
2	6	4¾	2	9	0	2	10	7
4	6	3	4	8	10	4	10	5
6	6	0	6	8	5	6	9	11¾
8	5	9	8	7	11	8	9	5½
10	5	6	10	7	6½	10	9	0
12	5	0½	12	6	9¾	12	8	2
14	4	5	14	5	11½	14	7	2
16	3	7	16	4	10	16	5	11¼
18	2	8¾	18	3	8	18	4	6
20	1	9	20	2	3¾	20	2	11½
21	1	1	21	1	6	21	2	0½
22	0	6	22	0	9½	22	1	1

1 S			1 H			2 S		
(2)	12	4½	(2)	13	1	(2)	13	3
2	12	4	2	13	0¾	2	–	–
4	12	2	4	12	11¼	4	–	–
6	11	10	6	12	9¼	6	13	0
8	11	4	8	12	4	8	12	9¾
10	10	9½	10	11	10¾	10	12	6
12	9	10½	12	11	3¼	12	12	1
14	8	10¾	14	10	4	14	11	5½
16	7	7	16	9	3	16	10	7
18	6	0	18	7	9	18	9	5½
20	4	1	20	5	8	20	8	6½
21	3	0	21	4	4½	21	6	4½
22	1	9	22	2	11½	22	4	8½

2 H			3 S			M Breadth		
(2)	13	3½	(2)	13	2	(2)	11	9
2	–		2	–	–	2	11	8
4	–		4	–	–	4	11	8
6	13	2½	6	13	6	6	11	7¼
8	13	0½	8	12	11½	8	11	6
10	12	10¾	10	12	9½	10	11	4½
12	12	7	12	12	7	12	11	2
14	12	2	14	12	3	14	10	11¼
16	11	6	16	11	10	16	10	7½
18	10	7½	18	11	5½	18	10	4
20	9	6½	20	10	8¼	20	9	11½
21	8	7	21	10	3	21	9	9
22	7	4	22	9	7¼	22	9	6¾

M Breadth Height			T Breadth Height		
(2)	13	10	(2)	16	8
6	13	10	6	16	8
8	13	11	8	16	9
10	14	1	10	16	10
12	14	4	12	17	0
14	14	8½	14	17	3
16	15	1½	16	17	6¼
18	15	7	18	17	9¾
20	16	1½	20	18	2
21	16	4½	21	18	4
22	16	8½	22	18	7

Sizes of scantlings

Sided	Inches	Moulded in midships	9ins
Floors in midships	11½	Moulded in midships	9ins
1 foothooks	10	ditto	7¾
2 ditto	8¾	ditto	6½
3 ditto at the head	8¾ }	= ditto	5½
at the top	7		
Top timbers	6½	ditto	4¾
Upper beams from	10½ to 8	ditto from 9¾ to 8 ins	
Lower beams from	12 to 11	ditto from 10 to 11	
Lower deck knees	7½		
Upper deck beams	5½		
Hooks from 10 to 8½ ins			

Dimensions of a schooner built by D. B. Davy for Messrs Hammick & Co. of Beer – the *Eliza*.

	Ft	ins
Length from fore perpendicular to timber K	3	6
Length from K to ⊠	19	4
Breadth of ⊠	0	10
Length from fore part of ⊠ to 15	29	2
Length from 15 to after part of stern post	2	5
	55	3

	Ft	ins
Room & space in fore body	1	9
Room & space in after body	1	8⅝
Half breadth moulded	9	1
Height of main *stem* I	15	0
Height of wing transom	[–]	[–]

Keel sided 10 inches in midships, fore and aft to 8½ ins
Stem sided at wales 10 ins, at the bottom to 8½
Floors sided from 10 ins to 8 inches *fore* and *aft*
1 foothooks sided 8 ins to 7 ins
2 [foothooks] and tops sided 6½ to 6 ins

Body plan	Ft	ins		Ft	ins
Guide up on middle line	2	11	Guide cut on base line	3	0½
F S	4	10¼	F S	5	10½
F H	6	1	F H	8	3
1 S	8	1¾	1 S up on side line	2	2
1H	10	1	1 H up on ditto	4	11½
			M B ditto	8	5
			T B ditto	10	9

		Ft	ins	Ft	ins	Ft	ins
Stem from perpendicular on the rabit [rabbet] line on keel		13	3	10	0	4	11

Stem from perpendicular line on the water lines		Ft	ins	Ft	ins	Ft	ins
	No 1	7	7	7	1	3	7½
	No 2	5	8½	5	5	2	10
	No 3	4	7½	4	4	2	3
	No 4	3	9	3	6½	1	9
	No 5	3	2	2	11¼	1	5
	No 6	2	9	2	6	1	2
	No 7	2	1½	1	10¾	0	9¼
	No 8	1	8½	1	6	0	5
	No 9	1	4	1	1¼	0	1
	No 10	0	11½	0	9	–	–

Height of water lines from rabbet line of keel		
	[Ft]	[ins]
No 1	1	1¾
2	2	3½
3	3	5¼
4	4	7
5	5	8¾
6	6	10½
7	8	10½
8	10	10½
9	12	10½
10	14	10½

	Ft	ins
Height of stem	15	0
Rabbet 2½ inches		
Height of wing transom	9	8

Fore body plan for ribbins [ribbands]

Guide	Ft	ins	F S			F H			1 S		
K	1	5	J	1	9	K	0	10½	K	2	4½
G	2	2½	H	3	1	J	2	9	J	4	5
F	2	9½	K	4	1	H	4	2	H	5	10½
D	3	4½	F	4	10	K[G?]	5	3¾	K[G?]	7	0
B	3	7½	D	5	10	F	6	1	F	7	9½
⊗	3	8½	B	6	4	D	7	4	D	8	11
			⊗	6	7½	B	7	11	B	9	5½
						⊗	8	2½	⊗	9	9

1 H			M B			T B			M B Height
K	3	10½	K	4	4¾	K	4	10	[Details
J	5	10½	J	6	2½	J	6	5¼	crossed out
H	7	2¾	H	7	4	H	7	4½	in MS. See
K[G?]	8	2½	G	7	11¾	G	7	11	below]
F	8	9½	F	8	3¾	F	8	2½	
D	9	8½	D	8	9¼	D	8	6½	
B	10	2	B	8	11½	B	8	8½	
⊗	10	3½	⊗	9	1	⊗	8	9½	

T B Height			M B Height		
K	12	4	K	10	7
J	12	2	J	10	2
H	12	0	H	9	10
G	11	10	G	9	6
F	11	8	F	9	0
D	11	5¼	D	8	10½
B	11	2½	B	8	6½
⊗	10	11½	⊗	8	4½

[After body plan]

Guide			F S			F H			1 S		
⊗	3	8½	⊗	6	7½	⊗	8	2½	⊗	9	9
2	3	7¾	2	6	6	2	8	1½	2	9	7½
4	3	7	4	6	3	4	7	9½	4	9	5
6	3	3¾	6	5	9	6	7	4	6	9	1½
8	2	11½	8	5	1	8	6	7	8	8	5½
10	2	5¼	10	4	2	10	5	6	10	7	7
12	1	10	12	3	2	12	4	3	12	6	2¾
14	1	1	14	1	10½	14	2	7	14	4	5
15	–	7¾	15	1	1	15	1	6½	15	3	4½
16	0	3	16	0	6¼	16	0	10¾	16	2	1¾

1 H			M B			M B Height			T B Height		
⊠	10	3½	⊠	9	1	⊠	8	4½	⊠	10	11½
2	10	2¼	2	9	0½	2	8	5	2	11	0
4	10	1	4	8	10¼	4	8	6½	4	11	0½
6	9	10	6	8	8½	6	8	8	6	11	1
8	9	4¼	8	8	6	8	8	10¾	8	11	2
10	8	10	10	8	3	10	9	2	10	11	4
12	8	0¼	12	8	0½	12	9	8	12	11	7
14	6	8	14	7	9	14	10	2½	14	11	10½
15	5	10	15	7	9½	15	11	6½	15	12	0
16	4	9	16	7	5	16	11	9¾	16	12	3

[Schooner *Swift*. A page of dimensions, crossed out in original MS.]
Dimensions as laid down of 1 vessel called the *Swift*, built for Captn Popham, which sailed very fast. Draft No [blank]

Water lines up from base line	Ft	ins			Ft	ins
			Stem from perpendiculars on baseline		12	2¼
			Stem from perpendiculars on water line			
No 1	1	1		No 1	8	7¼
2	2	2½	Stem up on timbers	2	6	10¼
3	3	4	K 4 8¾ Ditto 1 4½	3	5	7¼
4	4	6½	J 2 7¾	4	4	8
5	5	9	H 1 4	5	3	11¼
6	6	10	G 0 7	6	3	4¼
7	8	2	F 0 0½	7	2	9¾
8	9	7		8	2	2¼
9	10	11		9		
10	12	1½		10	1	9
				11	1	4½

	Ft	ins			
Stem from perpendicular on base line				6	1½
Length from perpendicular to the part of ⊠	24	3	No 1	4	9½
			2	3	10⅝
Breadth of ⊠	0	11	3	3	2⅓
Length from ⊠ to the after part of stern post	30	11	4	2	8
			5	2	2¾
			6	1	11
	56	1	7	1	6
			8	1	0¾
			9	0	8¾
			10	0	4½

[ROBERT DAVY'S SHIPS]

Names of different Navy ships built by Robt Davy, Topsham, from 1800 to
1814. [Year supplied from various sources]

					Built	[Year]
No	1	*Adder*	gun brig	12 guns	at Gulpit	[1813]
	2	*Clinker*	gun brig	12 guns	at Topsham	[1813]
	3	*Cephalus*	brigantine	18 guns	at ditto	[–]

[J. J. Colledge in *Ships of the Royal Navy*, 1969, Volume 1, records that the brig-sloop *Cephalus*, 18
guns, was launched in 1807 by Custance of Yarmouth. Robert Davy, however, built a similar
'Cruizer' class sloop, the *Scylla*, not listed above; her departure from the Exe for Plymouth to be
fitted out was reported in *Woolmer's Exeter & Plymouth Gazette*, 3 August 1809. The sailing
lighter listed as No 19 was possibly the *Falmouth*, a schooner-rigged vessel of that type, 160 tons,
built at Topsham in 1807.]

	4	*Conflict*	gun brig	12 guns	at Gulpit	[1805]
	5	*Daphne*	22 gun ship		at Topsham	[1806]
	6	*Hind*	20 gun sloop		at ditto	[1814]
	7	*Pelican*	brigantine	18 guns	at ditto	[1812]
	8	*Rapid [i]*	gun brig	12 guns	at Gulpit	[1804]

[The gun-brig *Rapid*, Lieutenant Henry Baugh, was sunk by gun batteries in the River Tagus
in May 1808.]

	9	*Rapid [ii]*	schooner	14 guns	at Topsham	[1808]
	10	*Safeguard*	gun brig	12 guns	at Gulpit	[1804]
	11	*Swinger*	gun brig	12 guns	at ditto	[1804]
	12	*Tartarus*	fire ship	24 guns	at Topsham	[1806]
	13	*Terror*	bomb		at ditto	[1813]
	14	*Tyne*	sloop	20 guns	at ditto	[1814]
	15	*Vesuvius*	bomb		at ditto	[1813]
	16	*Wasp*	brigantine	18 guns	at ditto	[1812]
	17	Mooring lighter			at Gulpit	[–]
	18	Mooring lighter			at Topsham	[–]
	19	Sailing lighter			at ditto	[–]

Names of different merchant ships built by Robt Davy [Years supplied as
above]

1	Ship *Earl St Vincent*	460 tons	built at Glasshouse	[1800]

[423 tons: *Lloyd's Register of Shipping* for 1820]

2	Ship *Caroline*	604 tons	at ditto	[1802]
3	Ship *Ann*		at ditto	[c. 1803]
4	Brig *Fly*		at ditto	[1803]

[The brig *Fly* is recorded in the Exeter Customs House Register of Shipping (Vol. 1, 1803 – No
56) as having been built not at Glasshouse but at Gulpit in 1803. It would also appear that the
sloop *Cynthia* (No 50) and the vessels numbered 5 to 10 in Davy's list were built at Gulpit.]

5	Smack *Alert*		at ditto	[1807]
	Omitted *Cynthea* [Sloop *Cynthia*, see No 50]			[1807]
6	Smack *Bristol Packet*		at ditto	
7	Schooner *Albion*		at ditto	[1808]
8	Schooner *Rebecca*		at ditto	[1809]
9	Brig *Segar*	260 tons	at ditto	[1809]

[184 tons and rigged as a snow: *Lloyd's Register* for 1820]

10	Sloop *Bicton* stone boat	at ditto	[c. 1812]
11	Brig *Arcade*	at Topsham	[1810]
12	Brig *Fortitude*	at Gulpit	[1810]
13	Ship *Phoenix*	at Topsham	[1810]
14	Ship *Jamaica Planter*	at Topsham	[1810]
15	Ship *Medina*	at Topsham	[1811]
16	Brig *Albion*	at Gulpit	[1811]
17	Brig *Susan*	at Topsham	[1812]
18	Brig *Brissett*	at Gulpit	[1812]
19	*Archable [Archibald]* brig	at ditto	[1814]

P.T. Over

Brought over

20	Smack *Alert*	built at Topsham	[1817]
21	Smack *Active*	at ditto	[1814]
22	Smack *Eagle*	at ditto	[1814]
23	Smack *Hawk*	at ditto	[1815]
24	Smack *Czar*	at Gulpit	[1814]
25	Schooner *Gleaner*	at Gulpit	[1814]
26	Brig *Flora*	at Topsham	[1815]
27	Smack *Exeter Packet*	at Gulpit	[1815]
28	Schooner *Britannia*	at Gulpit	[1815]
29	Schooner *Friends*	at ditto	[1815]
30	Smack *Bee*	at Topsham	[1815]
31	Smack *Sarah Anna*	at ditto	[1815]
32	Snow *Harriet*	at Topsham	[1815]
33	Snow *Brothers*	at ditto	
34	Snow *Heroine*	at ditto	[1816]
35	Smack *Two Brothers & Sisters*	at Gulpit	[1816]
36	*Viscount Exmouth* brig	at ditto	[1816]
37	*Peace* stone boat	at ditto	[1802]

[Built at Glasshouse not Gulpit: Exeter Customs House Registers, Vol. 1 (1802, No. 32).]

38	*Plenty* stone boat	at Topsham	[1805]
39	Smack *Nunsuch [Nonsuch]* (well vessel)	at ditto	[1816]
40	Smack *Agenoria*	at Gulpit	[1816]

Carried up

Brought up

41	Schooner *Jane & Harriet*	built at Topsham	
42	Schooner *Mary*	at ditto	[1816]
43	Schooner *Favourite*	at Gulpit	[1817]
44	Galliot *Fly*	about 50 tons	at Topsham	
45	Galliot *Active*	about 50 tons	at ditto	
46	Galliot *Lark*	ditto	at Gulpit	[left-hand
47	Galliot *Alert*	ditto	at [blank]	margin]
48	Galliot *Star*	ditto	at [blank]	Built in
49	Galliot *Dove*	ditto	at [blank]	1817
50	Smack *Cynthea [Cynthia]* omitted at No 6	at Gulpit	[Except
51	Schooner *Venus* built at Gulpit by [Thomas] Bishop		*Cynthia*]
52	Brig *Sedulous* built at Gulpit by [Thomas] Bishop		
53	Stone boat *Ceres* built at Topsham [by] T.B.		

[Thomas Bowden]

54   Brig *Mary* built at Topsham [by] T.B. [Thomas Bowden]
55   Sloop yatch [yacht] built at Topsham [by] T.B.
      [Thomas Bowden]   [left-
56   Schooner *Perseverance* built at Topsham [by] T.B.   hand
      [Thomas Bowden]   margin]
57   Sloop *Friends*   built at Gulpit   Built in
58   Schooner *Three Sisters* built at Topsham [by] T.B.   1818
      [Thomas Bowden]
59   Brig *Exeter* built at Wear [by] Thos Bishop 140 tons
                        Carried over

No   Brought over names and numbers
      1819
60   Smack *Edinburgh Castle*   built at Topsham   [1819]
61   Sloop *Eclipse* stone boat   built at Gulpit   [1819]
62   Smack or yacht *Regent*   built at Topsham   [1819]
63   Sloop *Hope*   built at Gulpit   [1819]
64   Sloop *Flower*   built at Topsham   [1819]
65   Sloop *Fortitude*   built at Topsham   [1820]
[66   omitted]
67   Sloop *Isabella*   built at Topsham   [1820]
68   Lighter *Majestic*   built at Topsham   [1820]
69   Schooner *Britannia*   built at Topsham   [1822]
70   Sloop *Good Intent*   built at Topsham   [1820]
71   Lighter *Neptune*   built at Topsham   [1823]
72   *Ace of Trumps*   built at Topsham   schooner   [1833]
73   *Post Boy*   built at Topsham   schooner   [1831]
74   *Racer*   built at Topsham   schooner   [1832]
75   *Amy*   built at Topsham   barque   [1839]
76   *Emelyn*   built at Topsham   barque   [1841]
77   *Clitus*   built at Topsham   brigantine   [1843]
78   *Sampson [Samson]* built at Topsham   ketch   [1843]
79   *Vansittart*   built at Topsham   schooner   [1834]
No80 Schooner *Swift*   built at Topsham   [1824]
81   Schooner *Ebenezer* built at Topsham   [1828]
82   – *Ceres* [see No 53] built at Topsham   [altered 1819]
83   Schooner *Eliza*   built at Topsham   [1826]
[–   Brig *Dorothea*   built at Topsham   1826]

[VALUATION OF ROBERT DAVY'S
SHIPPING PROPERTY]

Danl B. Davy's valuation of stone boats, lighters and shipping property belonging to Robert Davy, his father, which was examined and agreed to by him as being about their supposed worth, December 17th, 1822, Topsham.

Peace stone boat		£ 450	0s 0d
Two lighters belonging to ditto called the			
Betsey & *Lion*		120	0 0
Friends Goodwill stone boat		500	0 0
Two lighters belonging to ditto called the			
Fox & *Barley Mow*		100	0 0
Lucy stone boat		400	0 0
Two lighters belonging to ditto called the			
Increase & *Tiger*		150	0 0
Spice Bowl stone boat		350	0 0
Two lighters belonging to ditto called the			
Hope & *Eliza*		100	0 0
Duniere stone boat		200	0 0
One lighter belonging to ditto called the			
Conqueror		100	0 0
Eclipse stone boat		500	0 0
Two lighters belonging to ditto called the			
Grayhound & *Fly*		150	0 0
	carried over	£3120	0 0
Brought over		£3120	0s 0d
Defiance coal lighter	(Pring skipper)	70	0 0
Plenty lighter	(Cobley skipper)	120	0 0
Elephant coal lighter	(Cobley skipper)	170	0 0
Commerce lighter	(Fish skipper)	260	0 0
Sloop *Active* Bristol trader		650	0 0
Sloop *Grace* Bristol trader		700	0 0
Half of *Ceres* schooner		650	0 0
⅛ of *Medina* ship		400	0 0
⅛ of sloop[s] *Flower, Hope, Good Intent*			
& *Fortitude* London traders		500	0 0
		6640	0 0
	[?]	400	0 0
		£6240	0 0

[LIME-BURNING AND LAND]
October 23rd, 1822

A calculation made this day on the cost of burning, labour & all other expences of a hogshead of lime, particulars as underneath make [made] by Mr Robert [Davy] & Daniel Davy.

	£	s	d		£	s	d
First cost of 45 tons or a load of stones at the quarry	2	5	0				
Skipper's wages per load	1	8	0				
Lightermen's wages per load	0	10	0				
Stone boat hire per load	1	10	0				
Lighter hire per boat load 45 tons	0	10	0	=	6	3	0
[?]						7	6

Say/The culm cost at the kilns 10s 6d per quarter, a quarter of culm makes 7 hogsheads of lime (*at least*) which makes a hogshead of lime cost in culm 1s 6d 1 6

	£	s	d		£	s	d
Say/Lime burner's wages per hogshead	0	0	3				
Rent of kilns per hogshead	0	0	2				
Repair of kilns, tools, horse and asse's [asses'] labour, expences of gurries &c &c	0	0	1	=	0	0	6

	£	s	d
carried up	0	2	0
The calculation of burning one hogshead of lime	£	s	d
Brought up	0	2	0

Say/ A load or 45 tons of stones makes generally from 65 to 70 hogsheads of lime, it is here reckoned to make 67½ hogsheads (that is one ton of stones makes 1½ hogsheads of lime) which ton 1   10
of stones (at £6 3s 0d per load of 45 tons) cost
2s 9d per ton; at which rate a hogshead of lime
would cost 1s 10d in stones

Total cost of burning a hogshead of lime .... = 3s 10d

NB The dung will make something to pay part of the expences for gurries, tools &c &c

NB A quarter of culm ought to make 7½ hogsheads of lime and generally does

NB We know a load (*or 45 tons*) of stones will make 67½ hogsheads of lime as an account was kept at Marsh [Kilns] of 100 loads which burnt 6910 hogsheads which the book will show say from the beginning of the year to September 30th, 1822, which made 69 hogsheads to the load

P T Over
Remarks brought over

NB We also know a quarter of culm will burn 7 hogsheads of lime as an account was kept at Marsh Kilns of what quantity 156 quarters burnt which was 1124 Hogsheads, 1 Bushel, 2 Pecks, which will make it 7¼ hogsheads to the quarter of culm; 83 quarters of culm burnt at Gulpit 605 Hogsheads, 2 Bushels, 1 Peck of lime making 7¼ hogsheads burnt by the quarter of culm.

October 23rd, 1822 [Signed] D. B. Davy

R[obert] Davy's own stone boats cost of 45 tons at Topsham

Rippers for 45 tons	£2 10s
Stone boat mens wages	1 10
Stone boat hire	1 6 3
	5 6 3

Say 45 tons ripping or first cost at quarry at 13½d } 2 10 0

Stone boat hire at 7d per ton to Topsham } 1 6 3

Wages to boatmen 8d [per ton] } 1 10 0

28½ 5 6 3

Total cost of a Rt Davys boat load of stones at Topsham amounts to 2s 4½d per ton

Rt Davy pays Thos Carnell for 33 tons of lime stones delivered at Topsham £2 1 0

Say 8d per ton wages for 33 tons 1 2 0

Say [7d] per ton boat hire 19 3

£2 1 3

Say 13½[d] per ton for first cost making it 2s 4½d per ton total cost at Topsham

April 22nd, 1825
[Signed] D. B. Davy

[Lime burnt at Robert Davy's kilns in 1822]

	quantity Hogs- bush- heads els pecks	price	£ s d
Quantity of lime burnt at Wear Kilns in the year 1822 up to December 14th	12,431 2 2	4s 6d	2797 2 10½
Say – Quantity of lime that will be burnt at Wear Kilns from December 14 to December 31, 1822	200 0 0	4s 6d	45 0 0
Quantity of lime ashes burnt at Wear Kilns in the year 1822 up to December 14th	1527 1 0	2s 3d	171 16 3½
Say – Quantity of lime ashes that will be burnt at Wear Kilns from December 14 to December 31, 1822	50 0 0	2s 3d	5 12 6
Quantity of lime burnt at Gulpit Kilns in the year 1822	9423 3 0	4s 6d	2120 6 10½
Quantity of lime ashes burnt at Gulpit Kilns in the year 1822	1164 1 1	2s 3d	130 19 8
Quantity of lime burnt at Marsh Kilns in the year 1822	7903 0 0	4s 6d	1778 3 6
Quantity of lime ashes burnt at Marsh Kilns in the year 1822	668 0 0	2s 3d	75 3 0
carried over Hogsheads	33,367. 3 3		£7124 4 8½

Brought over Hogsheads	33,367	3	3		£7124	4	8½
Quantity of lime burnt at Lympstone Kilns in the year 1822 }	3706	0	0	4s 6d	833	17	0
Quantity of lime ashes burnt at Lympstone Kilns in the year 1822 }	231	0	3	2s 3d	26	0	6
	37,305	0	2		7984	2	2½

[To obtain the information given here about the kilns at Marsh and Lympstone, D. B. Davy wrote two letters, both of which are preserved in his Memoranda Book among the various loose papers. The tone is commanding. One of the letters is addressed to 'John Gore, St Georges Clist [Clyst St George]']

Topsham, December 15th, 1822

John Gore/

Send me in by the bearer the exact quantity of lime and the exact quantity of ashes you have burnt this year at Marsh Kilns; if there is any left in the kiln say about what quantity it is; also, send if you know the quantity of culm you have burnt. I am.

Yours &c
Danl B. Davy

[Reply overleaf:]

Lime	Ashes
7893	668
About 10 hogsheads in kiln	
7903	668.

About 20 quarters left. I don't [k]now the quantity of culm I have for the year 1822.

[The reply to the other letter is dated Lympstone, December 16th, 1822:]

Sir,

The quantity of lime burnt is 3706 hogsheads and ye ashes 231 hogsheads 3 bush[e]l: 567 quarters of culm landed. Sir, I should have wrote so as you may have had it by post tomorrow morning but [I] was not home in time for the post. From your obedient servant

Richard Denley [or Denby]

['The stones are brought up from the waterside, on horseback, or upon asses; and, being distributed around the top of the kiln, are there broken, and thrown into the kiln with shovels . . . The fuel chiefly, or wholly, Welsh culm. Lime is separated into two sorts at the kiln. Those who carry it to a great distance, on horseback, take only the clean knobs, or "stone-lime"; the ashes and rubbish being sold, at a lower price, to those who have lands at a shorter distance from the kilns, under the name of 'lime ashes' (*The Rural Economy of the West of England* by Mr Marshall, 1796, pp. 157–8). The writer goes on to describe how the lime was used to dress the fields; elsewhere, he mentions lime ashes 'for the use of the mason'. For an account of 'The technique of lime burning' see David Evans, *Devon & Cornwall Notes & Queries*, Vol. XXXVI (1987), pp. 34–5.]

[Loose paper not in D. B. Davy's handwriting: the cost of producing 65 hogsheads of lime at an estuary kiln.]

	£	s	d
First cost of stones	2	12	6
Skip[p]ers wages with thier monthly pay included	1	17	0
Boat hier	2	0	0
Lighterage	0	10	0
Lighter hier or use of the lighters	0	10	0
Burning with the cost of bringing the stones up &c &c at 6d	1	12	6
Culm for burning 65 hogsheads which a boat of stones ought to make	6	0	0
Common interest of mony for 12 months for amount laid out in burning a load of stones	0	15	0
Expences in collecting, rent of kilns, keeping in repairs, tools repaing [sic] taxes &c &c say	0	0	6
	15	17	6

An account of Mr Robt Davy's land measared [measured] January 1818.

At Wear in the parish of Topsham

	A[cres]	R[oods]	P[oles]		A	R	P
Brick Field	1	0	34				
Lower Hill head	1	3	34				
Higher Hill head	3	0	8				
Poltone Orchard	1	0	12				
Kiln Orchard	0	2	5				
Mogridges	0	2	29 =		8	2	2

At St Georges Clist & Sowton parish

	A	R	P			A	R	P
Ducks Marshes		[blank]						
Lower Marsh	8	1	5					
Middle Marsh	3	0	0					
Higher Marsh	7	0	22					
House & garden plot	0	0	31	=		18	2	18
Smith House & garden	0	0	36					
Sprages Orchard	0	0	32					
Town Me[a]dow total 3	2	5						
Robt Davy's part of ditto	0	1	38	[=]		1	2	26
			carried over			28	3	6

Clist Moor 1/9

	[Acres	Roods	Poles]
Mr Robert Davy's part of ditto			
Havels Field	3	1	17

	A	R	P
Lee's Meadow	2	2	24
Mr Robt Davy's part of ditto	0	3	22

Mr [Robert] Davy's lands at Topsham & D. B. Davys
measured in 1827

	A	R	P	[£ s d]
Lord Nelsons Inn & Timber Field	1	0	37	4 0 0
Bowling Green Field	1	2	10	7 0 0
Boat Field	3	1	10	£12 0 0
Boat Field Marsh	2	3	15	£8 0 0
Wood House Field (late Brands)	2	3	21	10 0 0
Owens Field on the Bowling Green	3	0	0	3 0 0
Rennells Field	4	3	27	£15 0 0
Warrens Closes/D. B. Davys	4	0	27	£20 0 0
Daggs two fields purchased of				
Mr Saml Hole/D. B. Davys	10	0	0	33 0 0
Bridge Field – D. B. Davy's	2	2	0	12 0 0
	36	1	27	£124 0 0

Mr [Robert] Davy's Church Lands at Topsham measured in 1827

		A	R	P	[s d]
Haydons 6 Acres		6	1	0	£17 0 0
Norrishes Field		2	0	35	£7 10 0
Sentry Hill Pond Field	say	4	0	0	£14 0 0
Sentry Hill Three-Acre Field	say	3	0	0	£9 0 0
Sentry Hill Middle Park Field	say	5	0	0	£17 0 0
		20	1	35	£64 10 0
		36	1	27	124 0 0
		56	3	22	£188 10 0

[Loose paper: Document addressed to D. B. Davy, Esq., and entitled 'Measurement of Parish of Topsham &c &c']

Parish of Topsham				Acres	roods	poles
Total survey by Poole				1553	2	10
Divided as follows						

	Acres	roods	poles			
Land	1334	1	17			
Disputed Marshes	25	0	11			
Beach Timber Yard	13	1	24			
Bowling Green	63	2	2			
Plantation 'Waste'	15	0	12			
Houses, gardens &c	97	3	21			
Not accounted for						
by Troake	4	1	3			
				1553	2	10

February 23, 1839

	A	R	P
Total land tytheable	1334	1	17
Annual value of ditto £3511 5 2			
Houses and gardens	97	3	21

Avarage [average] annual value of land per acre £2 12 6

February 22, 1839

[A second Davy volume

A substantial volume of additional material, which apparently owes its survival to its re-use as a post office account book, can be seen on application at the Devon Record Office, ref. 62/3. The index entry describes it as a letter book of the shipping firm of D. B. Davy of Topsham, 1834–1838, giving details of shipments and names of ships; with, further on in the volume, the accounts of Topsham Post Office, 1929–*c*1950. The Davy section consists of copies in various hands of letters sent out by the firm, many dealing with day-to-day matters such as the recovery of overdue bills and the movements of Davy-owned vessels, among them the *Ceres*, *Active* and the barge *Darby Allen*. The sale of anchors and chain cables feature prominently and there are letters on the firm's imports of hemp from St Petersburg, now Leningrad. In a letter dated 11 September 1835 to Mr Alex Cunningham of Southampton, on the appointment of a foreman to superintend repairs, stores and materials, it was pointed out that 'our business as shipbuilders is very small'. Among other recipients of letters were shipbuilders at Cowes, Bridport and Guernsey. It is the editor's hope that further Davy material, including perhaps photographs of the shipbuilders, will come to light following this present publication.]

APPENDIX A

[The text printed here is taken from a copy given to the late Miss Dorothy Holman by a visitor to her museum in Topsham. Unfortunately, the transcriber left several blanks and clearly had difficulties in deciphering the names of some of the ships mentioned. Other sources have been drawn upon to make good these deficiencies as far as possible. A few corrections have been made concerning tonnage and dates and the names of two warships, *Traveller* and *Greyhound*, supposedly built by Robert Davy but not listed in official records, have been omitted. Marginal headings which add nothing to the text have also been omitted to save space. All editorial changes or additions are contained within square brackets.]

BIOGRAPHY OF MR ROBERT DAVY
OF COUNTESS WEAR, DEVON

Born October 20th, 1762; died August 30th, 1862, aged 99 years and 10 months

Memorandum. This was written by Francis, youngest son of Mr Robert Davy, about 6 months prior to his father's death; the last few lines being added after that occurrence.

Mr Robert Davy was the eldest son of the late Mr James Davy, who died at Countess Wear in the parish of Topsham in the year 1813, aged 84 years. Mr James Davy carried on the business of lime and coal merchant, in addition to which he farmed the *then* whole of the estate known as Wear Barton. The barton, or farm house &c, was situated adjoining the south side of Glasshouse Lane, then belonging to Wm Spicer Esq., who died at Wear House in 1788, afterwards to his son Francis Spicer, who died at Courtlands in the parish of Lympstone in 1853, which said Francis Spicer Esq sold off sundry portions of the estate to different people at various periods; but in 1804 Mr Spicer sold the whole of the remaining portion of the estate together with Wear House to the late Admiral Sir [John Thomas] Duckworth, Bart.[1] The farm house, Wear Barton, after Mr James Davy left it to go up to Countess Wear in 1782 to occupy a property which he had purchased there a year or so previous, and where he built limekilns &c, was converted into cottages, and was burnt down by an incendiary in 1838 by a person, a stranger in the neighbourhood, who had on the same day only come out of the County Prison where he had been confined for some offence.

Mr Robert Davy was born at Mare Farm at [?Whipton][2] in the parish of Heavitree on October 20th, 1762. He was brought down to Wear Barton

---

[1] Memorial in Topsham Parish Church: Admiral Sir John Thomas Duckworth, KGCB, died in chief command of His Majesty's ships at Plymouth, 31 August 1817, aged 69 years.
[2] The 1844 Tithe Map for the parish of Heavitree includes as part of Whipton Barton Mareford Orchard (No. 862) and Mare (No. 863), three acres of arable land: Devon Record Office, Tithe Apportionment, Heavitree, 1844, p. 29.

when about 3 years of age, about which period his father took Wear Barton
to rent of Mr Wm Spicer (1766). Mr Robert Davy married, July 9th
[1792],[3] Miss Grace Bishop, daughter of [blank] Bishop Esq, a landed
proprietor who resided in the parish of Bradninch, by whom he had 6 sons
and 3 daughters, of whom 4 sons and 1 daughter are now [1862] living. He
was educated at Topsham and Bridgwater. About the year 1790 his father
gave up the whole of his business to him. Near this period, 1789, he built the
house [at Countess Wear] in which he resided up to the time of his death,
and which is now occupied by his 4th son, Mr Samuel Bishop Davy.[4]

Though not brought up to the business of a shipbuilder, more than
perhaps having gained a little insight into it simply by his father building
and repairing barges for conveyance of coal, culm and limestone up the
river and from Babbacombe and the neighbourhood of Torbay, he
commenced shipbuilding at Glasshouse (so called on account of there being
on the site a glass manufactory, the tower of which was taken down about
1777), and launched the ships into 'Glasshouse Gut'. Probably people, a
few years hence, will scarcely credit that vessels, particularly of so large a
tonnage, were ever built here. The following are the names of some of the
vessels:–

Grace	West Indiaman	[228] tons	fitted out and
Earl St Vincent	ditto	[423] ditto	sent direct to
Mary	ditto	[200] ditto	Jamaica.

Caroline (in 1802), afterwards called the *Batavia*, 604 tons, East Indiaman;
with many other vessels.

Several of them he was part-owner of with London West India
merchants. The owners of the *Caroline* presented Mr Robert Davy with a
painting of her in full sail, which is hung over the chimney-piece at his
residence at Countess Wear [Plate 1]. She is supposed to have been the
largest ship ever built within the estuary of the River Exe.

About 1802 he gave up shipbuilding at Glasshouse in consequence of
some disagreement with Mr Spicer, the then owner of the property, and
commenced building a little higher up 'Glasshouse Gut' by the limekilns
called 'Gullpit'. Here he also built a great many vessels of all descriptions.
The following are the names of a few: [*Adder, Conflict, Rapid, Safeguard* and
Swinger, gun-brigs, for the Government;]

[*Archibald*],	West Indiaman,	[274] tons;
[*Brissett*],	ditto	[207] tons;
[*Segar*],	ditto	[184] tons;

besides 'dockyard lumps' and vessels for the London trade and other
coasting trades. In 1820 the shipbuilding here was finally closed. The
blacksmith's shop, now [1862] standing on the edge of the Gut, is the only
remains of the shipbuilding trade which was once carried on at this spot. A
person by the name of Wm Rowden, a smith, still continues to occupy the
shop; he has been in Mr Davy's employment as smith for upwards of 50
years.

[3]By licence at Topsham Parish Church, Thomas Manning, Mary Davy, Sarah Eustace and
Tho. Johns, witnesses (Topsham parish register).
[4]Known at one time as The Poplars, also as Withymead; now Waring Bowen House (British
Rheumatism & Arthritis Association).

The trouble and expense to get so large vessels down the Gut and the river must have been immense, floating them on casks, lifting them also by barges fastened down to them by chains, besides the difficulties of wharfing and towing them in such a shallow narrow channel, far different from having a steam tug to tow them steadily, as also to give them a constant steerage way through the water, comparatively as a horse would draw a cart, no sheering about with the least air of wind so as to ground them.

About 1803 or 1804 Mr Davy purchased a property at the extreme north end of the town at Topsham called Passage, which premises he enlarged by extending them towards low water, forming slipways &c, for the purpose of building and repairing ships. He here built many for the Government, one 22 guns frigate, 540 tons, named the *Daphne*, also gun-brigs, bomb and [fire-] ships, besides a great number of merchant ships from 500 tons downwards, several of which he held parts of. One was called the *Jamaica Planter*, which was licensed to carry 45 armed men. She was fitted out at Topsham at a cost of £18,000 and sent to Jamaica, but was lost on her [second] passage home laden with sugar &c. In fact she was never heard of, and neither she nor the cargo were but very insufficiently insured. He also built a number of large smacks, 200 tons register, commonly known by the name of 'Scotch smacks', to carry passengers and goods to and from London to Scotland, the fitting up and furniture &c of the cabin fare of which smacks cost upwards of £1,100. He sent down the river at one tide 4 Government vessels, namely, a corvette, bomb [ship] and 2 gun-brigs, on their way to be delivered to the respective naval yards, for at that period builders had to deliver the ships at their own expense and risk at the naval yards as per contract.

At one period Mr Davy had ships building at one place and the other of various tonnage amounting on the whole to upwards of 1,800 tons. He was so exact and prompt in completing his Government contracts within the time specified, that he never had any complaint, while many others were *fined most heavily*. But when the Government offered handsome premiums per day during the hottest part of the war, just prior to the close of it, about say 1812 to 1815, to all those who would complete their contracts prior to the time stated, he received very large sums in that shape, having finished *all* his ships more or less before the time. The Admiralty offered him as a mark of appreciation several more ships to build, and sent men to survey the river to induce him to go on; but, in consequence of his health at this period (about 1815–16) getting rather indifferent together with his eyesight beginning to fail, he declined the offer. He gave up the shipbuilding here (Passage) in 1826 to his son Daniel Bishop Davy, who had assisted him for several years and who was now about 27 years of age.

About the year 1820 he commenced the trade of selling bar iron at Passage, Topsham; also, about the same period or a year or so subsequently, he commenced the manufacturing of chain cables and anchors; and about 1821 or 1822 he took off the iron, hemp and tallow business of Mr Robert Roger Sanders at Palace Gate, Exeter, and purchased at the same time the premises of him, and commenced importing hemp and tallow. He carried on the whole for a year or so on his own account, when he took his second son, Mr Daniel Bishop Davy (born 1799), who had assisted him, into partnership, and about 1825 he gave up the whole of this business to this son. It may be truly said that from 1790 to about 1825 he was the largest lime burner, coal merchant and shipbuilder in the West of England; also he farmed and grazed very extensively; and he did a little in the Newfoundland trade, besides selling large quantities of oak timber and bark &c.

In the year 1834 Mr Robert Davy took his fourth surviving son, Samuel Bishop Davy (born 1807) into partnership to carry on the coal, lime and farming business [margin: 'at Countess Wear'] as well as ship-owning, which partnership has continued up to his (Mr Robert Davy's) death.

Mr Robert Davy was greatly instrumental in getting the Bar at Exmouth first buoyed, through the late Lord Rolle, whose attention he drew to it and pressed on him to assist.

He was solely the means of compelling the old Corporation of Exeter to erect the [canal] locks just above the ferry at Topsham. A very expensive course of law proceedings ultimately ended in a compromise, Mr Davy finding the stone. The going to law, together with the stone, must have cost Mr Davy at least £800.[5]

He remembered the year before Countess Wear Bridge was built, say in 1772, when three men and a horse were drowned in one day in endeavouring to ford the river, when the floods and tide were high, they being strangers. Mr Robert Davy, *at his own expense*, and for giving a better passage for his barges, particularly during floods, converted two arches into one in the year 1842. The contract price for so doing was £430; altogether this work must have cost him nearly £500.

He was chiefly instrumental in getting Topsham Bridge being made a county bridge, which was done at Easter 1830.

He remembered when the tower of the Glasshouse, which stood at the corner at the west end of the Glasshouse Lane (now a garden occupied by Captain Templeman), was taken down. Schoolboys used to endeavour to throw stones over it, and it was decided to take it down. As it had been struck with lighning and injured, the difficulty was how it was to be taken down. At last, by some means, they got large pieces of timber in under, a little distance up, to take a great portion of the weight. The timber was then set on fire, and when it was burnt through, down fell the tower.

He used to talk of the first American War in 1774: for, as a boy, he heard an observation made at the time by a Topsham merchant, when the two ships went down Channel for America with the Tea and Stamp Act: 'There goes the bane of old England'. He frequently used to repeat a toast that was drunk at parties during Lord North's administration: 'May Lord North have a continual itching without any scratching until he has made peace with America'.

As a boy he remembered the present Mr Benjamin Buttall's grandfather in 1779 with others (he, Mr Buttall [Buttell], being captain), who fitted out a ship named *King George*, about 400 tons register, as a privateer, which carried 24 guns and 150 men. She was placed on the 'Hard' opposite Topsham Churchyard on a *Sunday* to 'grave', or clean her bottom. She went

[5]For further details see Devon Record Office, Exeter City Archives, Law papers, Box 20, Attorney General & Exeter v Davy 1827.

to sea a few days after, and was never heard of. It was supposed that she foundered and that all the crew were drowned, she being a very old vessel.[6]

Mr Robert Davy was taken entirely blind in 1816 on his way to London by coach. He had complained of his sight failing before. He, without the least preparation, had at once a very severe operation performed by a Mr Alexander, which resulted in a complete failure. This failure was attributed partly to the fact that the operation was performed too hastily owing to his body not being in a fit state, not having been prepared, and partly to the fact that the medical man attempted too much by performing on *both* eyes at once, when he ought not to have attempted but on one only. After suffering a good deal of violent inflammation, [blank] &c, he was brought home after 10 to 12 months to Countess Wear. After a while (say, about 1818) he went to Exmouth, where he bathed, and where he was constantly attended by Dr Samuel Barnes; and, when he had recovered strength, he made up his mind to undergo another operation. Sir Wm Adams was engaged to come to Exeter to perform it. Consequently lodgings were taken in Magdalene Street for the better convenience of being attended during the operation and after by Dr Barnes and others. Mr Robert Davy, on a Good Friday afternoon, walked in from Wear to the great sorrow and grief of his children, fearing the result.

The operation was performed: the right eye was entirely gouged out, and something was done to the left eye. The operation was most severe, and the constant bleeding that had to be kept up was most extraordinary. He partially recovered his sight in his left eye, and was again able to ride and walk about in the immediate neighbourhood, as also to write a letter, for 5 or 6 years. Then his sight again began to fail; and he was obliged to give up riding his pony. However, he continued to walk a great deal, say, from about six o'clock in the morning until evening (saving at his meals) to Topsham, Exeter, and over his farm – 10 to 20 miles a day, guided by a boy. This he continued until about 1840, when his legs began to fail him, when he first commenced being driven in a little four-wheeled carriage.

About 1820 he commenced looking into and devoting a great deal of his time to parochial matters, in which he took a very lively interest, principally in regard to the poor. He was the means of getting rid of that costly nest of vice and dissipation, the *[Topsham] Common Workhouse*, (in 1825), which was situated in Higher Passage Lane [now Follett Road], on the site of which Clara Place is built. Old, middle age, young and infants, bad and good, were huddled together. When this establishment was broken up, they were allowed to go where they liked to reside, and money was paid to them weekly according to circumstances.

Mr Robert Davy was elected one of the first Guardians at the commencement of the Union in 1836, and continued to be so until, from his

[6]For accounts of Captain Buttell's privateering activities, first in the *Molly* and then in the *King George*, see Hugh Wilson Holman, 'Topsham privateer, *King George*, 1779', *Devon & Cornwall Notes & Queries* VII (1914–15), pp. 17–22 and David J. Starkey, 'A note on the privateering career of the *King George*, 1779', *Devon & Cornwall Notes & Queries* XXXV (1986), pp. 365–8. Topsham Museum has an original poster, dated 8 January 1779, offering 'gentlemen seamen and young able-bodied landmen' the chance to make their fortunes on a six-month cruise on the *King George*, and similar notices appeared in the *Exeter Flying-Post* 15 January and 5 February 1779.

advanced age (say, 99 years and 5 months) and incapability, he caused a letter (dated February 7th, 1862) to be written to the chairman at the Board of St Thomas' Union, tendering his resignation &c. The board, at their meeting, passed a complimentary resolution, and desired their clerk (Mr Bidwell) to send it to him. He was scarcely ever known to be absent from attending the board both on Mondays and Fridays until the last 12 months. Moreover, he seldom missed being at the Vestry at Topsham, when the poor were paid, to hear their applications, &c. He always advocated the part of the poor, and was much respected and paid attention to by all his brother-Guardians.

From his youth he felt a great interest in politics and public affairs generally. Few men kept themselves more acquainted with what was moving in the world than he did. For a person in his position he had a wonderful influence for miles around – Topsham, Exeter, and (specially) Crediton. He *discussed* public matters *freely*. He was a devoted Whig; and he lent a very great aid, both in person and *purse*, in the various hard-contested elections; and that too prior to about 1830 when men who took an active part, and expressed their opinions on that side of politics, were looked on very differently to what they now are. In those days they were almost despised, and called 'Jacobites' and so on: indeed at one period they were obliged to be very careful how they expressed themselves, and were indeed at one time obliged to make themselves rather scarce.

He took a lively interest in Queen Caroline's trial; and, when she was acquitted, he was the means, with others, of getting up a great fete for the poor. He, with others, walked in procession through the town and burnt the 'Green Bags'[7] on the beach at the bottom of the town, and had dinner, tea, dancing, &c, for the whole parish in a field called the Timber field behind the Lord Nelson Inn.

He was always a firm supporter of the Church, and make a rule to attend regularly twice a day. Though a man of warm temperament, e.g. when excited, or [when] things did not go according to his wishes in business or otherwise, or when put out by his labourers not doing as he wished and so on, he would make use of all sorts of queer, odd and personal expressions (and no distinction was made to any person, rich or poor, neither did he whisper, for he had a most powerful voice) to give vent to his wrath or anger; yet those in his employ in his early days, as well as others, have stated that he was never known to take the Lord's name in vain, nor to swear, nor to make use of any blasphemous language. It is true that many in quoting him at such times, have put such expressions as coming from him *as a matter of course*, but when their attention was drawn to it, and they were asked pointedly if he or they had heard him make use of such words, they were obliged to acknowledge that they had not, but that, hearing him give vent loudly and in an excited state, they took it for granted that he must be making use of the ordinary too common blasphemous foul language; but his growl was always worse than his bark. He has been known on more than one occasion to discharge persons in the midst of their work for swearing. On one occasion he was in an adjoining field to that in which one of his men

[7]Green bag: 'used formerly by barristers and lawyers for documents and papers' (*Shorter Oxford English Dictionary*).

was ploughing with oxen driven by a youth; he overheard the man cursing and swearing to such a degree, that he immediately stopped the plough, had the oxen unyoked, and discharged the man instantly (the man having been cautioned before by him). Many of his quaint expressions will be found in the old dictionaries, such as Bailey's.

He was always a most extremely active man, particularly prior to his being taken blind. Seldom, if ever, in his bed after 5 o'clock in the morning, he would think nothing of riding 20, or even, 30 miles before breakfast; he would often ride to Plymouth and back in the same day. With the exception of being blind, and the effects of it, he always enjoyed very good health. No amount of exertion seemed to have any effect; whatever hour he went to bed, nothing ever interfered with his sleep, and he would be up as early as usual the next morning. He was a man of great hospitality, and in his prime few men enjoyed themselves more or were more fond of having their friends about them. He was acknowledged to be a man of great talent and ability, and his memory was extraordinarily retentive.

Throughout his life he has been an extraordinary man. He was a good husband and kind father, and a friend to the poor. Few men kept their workmen longer in their employment. Naturally, those who were with him when he commenced business have gone to their long home; but a few years ago there were those who had been from 40 to 60 years in his service.

Speaking of his wife since her death, he used to say that he had been blessed with one of the best wives man ever had. She too was an extraordinarily clever, active business-like managing person, a kind and affectionate wife and mother, and a friend to the poor.

He continued to ride out in his fly almost every day as far as his son's house at Palace Gate, Exeter, and back. Gradually getting weaker, he none the less (in spite of failing memory) perfectly understood everything that was said, and asked very reasonable questions about the weather and what was going on, although he did not long retain what was said to him. The last time that he rode out was on Monday, the 25th August, when (it being a very cold windy day for the season of the year) it is supposed that he caught a slight cold. He took to his bed, got weaker and wasted fast, evidently showing that his time was near. He refused to take almost any kind of nourishment: in fact during the last fortnight he would take nothing except that which was forced upon him – and that was very little. He appeared to be in no pain, and said nothing, but evidently had his reason about him to the last. About 12 o'clock on Friday night he was helped out and into bed by his man, Vickery: he did not move afterwards. At a quarter to three o'clock on Saturday morning, the 30th August 1862 he made a very slight cough and expired without a struggle. Indeed he, as it were, slept away, aged 100 years less 51 days. He was buried in the family vault at St Mary's Clist [Clyst St Mary] Churchyard on September 5th 1862, Friday morning about 12 o'clock.

Francis Davy

Notes appended by Mr Francis Davy (whose signature is above).
Countess Wear Bridge built 1772
Alphington Bridge over Alphington Brook just beyond Countess Wear Bridge, built 1775.

Mr Robert Davy converted at his own expense two arches of Countess Wear Bridge into one. Cost him £439: contract, August 29th 1842, builder Wm Dawe.

Mr James Davy, father of the above, built Lime Kilns Quay &c 1780.

Mr James Davy left the house Wear Barton, south side of Glasshouse Lane, to go to Countess Wear to reside 1782, having purchased the house &c there, where he died in 1813.

[Added in another hand] Reputed to have made £100,000.

[The tomb in Clyst St Mary churchyard with its inscriptions can still be seen (1988). There is also a memorial commemorating Robert Davy and his wife Grace (who died on 5 June 1839, aged 75) on the north wall of the north transept of Topsham parish church, erected by Francis Davy, 'residing at Rivers-meet in this parish, who died 10th September 1896, aged 86 years'. Although the originals appear to have been destroyed during the Exeter Blitz, transcripts of various Davy wills have survived in the Westcountry Studies Library, Exeter, including those of Francis Davy, James Davy (died 1813) and Robert Davy himself, who left an estate sworn at under £25,000. One of Robert Davy's brothers, James, went to Jamaica; another, Thomas, was a doctor at Ottery St Mary. Dr Edward Davy (1806–85), son of the latter, is listed in the *Dictionary of National Biography* and similar works; he helped to pioneer the electric telegraph, and in 1839 went out to Australia. Another of Thomas's sons, Henry, was the father of Sir Henry Davy, a leading Exeter physician knighted in 1919.

Extracts from the biography of Robert Davy were published in the August and September 1971 issues of *Estuary*, the Topsham community magazine, and by C. N. Ponsford in *Topsham and the Exe Estuary*, Exeter, 1979. It also seems to have formed the basis for obituaries that were published in Exeter newspapers after his death in 1862; but it has never previously been printed in its entirety.]

[POSTSCRIPT

The Rev. John Swete's 'Picturesque Sketches of Devon' (Devon Record Office, ref. 564 M) include descriptions and watercolours of Robert Davy's kilns at Countess Wear, in vol. 18, and at Marsh on the river Clyst, vol. 8. The artist was particularly attracted by the Gulpit kiln, served by 'a creek [Glasshouse Gut] into which the barges laden with stone and culm insinuate themselves'. He noted that 'the arches and the rude masonry of this structure were most beautifully decorated by vines of an old growth, which spread their lateral branches over the higher part of the walls; where, open to the influence of the sun and the artificial warmth communicated by the unremitting fires of the kiln, they became unusually productive . . . To these kilns of Mr Davis [Davy] the resort of farmers with their carts, waggons and pack horses, was astonishing, and the demand for lime as manure far exceeded the supplies of his kilns' (vol. 18, pp. 159–160). Swete also noted that at the time of this visit, in the summer of 1799, he observed 'from the road near to Mr Davis' lime-kilns, the skeleton of a vessel of very considerable size, which was there on the stocks and intended for the West India trade. To questions which I put to one of the shipwrights respecting its burthen and the safety of launching her in so narrow a channel and at such a distance from the main river, I was answered that it would be about 400 tons, and that tho' it was the largest vessel ever built on the Exe, there would be but little hazard in committing her to the water' (p. 167). This ship was probably the *Earl St Vincent*, 423 tons, built in the Glasshouse yard and completed the following year.]

Appendix B

EXTRACTS FROM EXETER NEWSPAPERS

WARSHIPS BUILT ON THE EXE BY ROBERT DAVY AND OTHERS

Trewman's Exeter Flying-Post 9 August 1804
Exeter . . . On Monday the 23rd ult was launched by Mr R. Davey, at his shipwright's-yard, Wear, near Topsham, the gun-brig *Safeguard*; and on Wednesday, the 25th, from the yard of Mr O. Ayles, the gun-brig *Piercer*. They are two of the numerous class now building in various parts of the kingdom. There is also building in this port three vessels of the same description, and three brigantines of war, calculated to carry eighteen 32-pound carronades.

Trewman's Exeter Flying-Post 30 August 1804
Plymouth . . . Sunday [26 August]. Wind variable, fair. Came in from Topsham, two beautiful gun-brigs, of 16 guns, and the *Tortoise*, dockyard lighter, under convoy of an hired cutter, and the direction of Mr Collins, one of the superintending masters of the ordinary in Hamoaze. They went up the harbour directly to be fitted for sea, and from those who understand shipbuilding, they are esteemed strong, well-built, servicable vessels, and do credit to Mr Davey and Mr O. Ayles, the builders, at Topsham.

Trewman's Exeter Flying-Post 13 September 1804
Exmouth. Arrived . . . *Tortoise* lighter, Blacker, from Plymouth, under convoy of the *Viper* cutter, with riggers and stores, for rigging a gun-brig built in this harbour.

Trewman's Exeter Flying Post 20 September 1804
Exmouth. Sailed . . . *Viper* cutter, Lieutenant Carpenter, for Plymouth, and the *Tortoise*, dockyard lighter, Blacker, convoy to a beautiful gun-brig [*Swinger*], built at Mr Davey's yard at Wear.

Trewman's Exeter Flying-Post 6 December 1804
Exmouth. Sailed . . . for Plymouth, the *Rapid*, Collins, and *Argent* [*Urgent*], Patterson, being two remarkably fine-looking brigs, built at this harbour, (viz), one at Mr Bass's yard, Lympston, the other at Mr Davey's at Wear, who sailed under convoy of the *British Fair* [hired cutter].

Trewman's Exeter Flying-Post 28 February 1805
Exmouth. Sailed . . . *Staunch* gun-brig, Lieut. Street, for Plymouth, convoy to the *Surinam* cutter brig, built at Mr Davey's yard in this port, a very handsome fast sailing vessel.
[According to other records the *Surinam* sloop-of-war was built by Obadiah Ayles, not Davy.]

Trewman's Exeter Flying-Post 2 May 1805
Exmouth. Sailed . . . the *Swinger*, gun-brig, Lieut. Ross, as convoy to the
Weazle sloop-of-war, launched at Mr Owen's yard, at Topsham, and copper
bottom'd here; she is by competent judges esteemed one of the best vessels
which have been built in this harbour.

Trewman's Exeter Flying Post 16 May 1805
Exmouth. Sailed . . . the *Cheerly*, gun-brig, Lieut. Montozue, for Plymouth,
convoy to the *Woolverine [Wolverine]* sloop-of-war, launched from Mr Owen's
yard, Topsham, and as complete a vessel as the *Weazle* lately launched
therefrom.

Trewman's Exeter Flying-Post 31 July 1806
Exmouth. Sailed . . . *Daphne* a 20 gun ship, built at Mr Davey's yard in this
fine harbour, for government, under convoy of the *Pickle* schooner, Lieut.
Gallaway, for Plymouth.
[This ship had 22 guns according to D. B. Davy's list and other records.]

Trewman's Exeter Flying-Post 6 November 1806
Plymouth. Wednesday [29 October]. Came in from Falmouth, with
convoy, the *Caroline* of 16, Lieutenant Derby: she sailed again directly for
Exmouth, with the *Camel*, Dockyard, Stonehouse, and *Bedford* navy
transports, with stores and rigging for the new sloops of war building at the
private yards at the port of Exmouth. Also, with old naval stores for the
same port, bought at the dockyard sales here, the *Good Friends* and *Sarah*.
Exmouth. Sailed . . . *Caroline* armed brig, Lieut. Derby, with the *Tortussa*
[Tartarus] fire-ship, built in the harbour, and *Tortoise* lump, Blakey, for
Plymouth.

Trewman's Flying-Post 20 November 1806
Exmouth. Sailed . . . *Cheerley [Cheerly]*, gun vessel, Lieut. Folleton, convoy
to the *Cyan[e]* sloop-of-war, and *Thunder* fire-ship, built in the private yards
in this port.
[Curiously, it would seem that the *Thunder* was in fact the *Lightning*, launched at Topsham by
Obadiah Ayles on 14 October 1806. She is referred to again in the next paragraph. *Cheerly* was
a Bridport-built gun-brig.]

Trewman's Exeter Flying-Post 26 November 1806
Plymouth. Friday [21 November]. Came in from Exmouth, the *Cheerly*
gun-brig, of 16, with the *Cyane*, of 18, a fine new sloop-of-war, and the
Thunder fire-ship, of 14, both built at that port; they came round under jury
masts, to be fitted for sea at this port.

Trewman's Exeter Flying-Post 29 January 1807, Exeter column dated
Wednesday 28 January
On Monday last [26 January] was launched from the building yard of Mr
Thomas Owen sen. of Topsham, a new sloop-of-war, called the *Porcupine*, a
strong well-finished ship, and an excellent model for a fast sailer. This
morning [28 January] she was towed from Topsham down the river to
Exmouth, there to have a temporary rigging, in order to be taken round to
Plymouth under the command of Mr Patterson.

Trewman's Exeter Flying-Post 26 February 1807
Exmouth. Sailed . . . that fine sloop-of-war that was built at Topsham, the
Porcupine, Thomas Peterson, master, for Plymouth, under convoy of the
Lady Warren.

Trewman's Exeter Flying-Post 21 May 1807
Exmouth. Sailed . . . the *Cheerly* gun-brig, to convoy the *Fawn* sloop-of-war,
which was built at Mr Owen's yard, Topsham.

Trewman's Exeter Flying-Post 24 September 1807
Exmouth. Sailed . . . that elegant new fire-ship *Erebus* which was built at Mr
Owen's yard, at Topsham, to be fitted out at Plymouth for his Majesty's
service.

Woolmer's Exeter & Plymouth Gazette 3 August 1809
Exmouth. Sailed . . . the *Sylla [Scylla]*, a fine new gun-brig [a sloop-of-war],
built at Topsham, for Plymouth, to be fitted for his Majesty's service.

Woolmer's Exeter & Plymouth Gazette 6 August 1812
Plymouth. Thursday [30 July]. Sailed his Majesty's gun-brig *Intelligent*,
with stores for the *Wasp* at Topsham.
Exmouth. Sailed . . . *Wasp*, a fine new sloop-of-war to be brig-rigged, built
at Topsham.
Plymouth. Saturday [1 August]. Arrived the *Wasp* from Topsham.

Woolmer's Exeter & Plymouth Gazette 27 May 1813
Exmouth. Sailed . . . the *Vesuvius*, a fine new sloop of war, built at Topsham,
bound to Portsmouth, commanded by Capt. John Parker of Exmouth.
[She was a bomb-ketch similar to *Terror* (see next extract).]

Woolmer's Exeter & Plymouth Gazette 5 August 1813
Exmouth. Sailed . . . the *Adder* and *Clinker* gun-brigs, and *Terror*, bomb, for
Portsmouth, to be fitted out for his Majesty's service, under convoy of the
Gambier cutter.

Woolmer's Exeter & Plymouth Gazette 2 April 1814
Exmouth. Sailed . . . the *Hind*, a fine new frigate, built at Mr Davy's yard,
Topsham, for Portsmouth, to be fitted out for his Majesty's service.

Woolmer's Exeter & Plymouth Gazette 25 June 1814
Exmouth. Sailed . . . the *Tyne*, a new brig of war, built at Topsham, under
convoy of the *Cracker*, gun-brig, for Portsmouth.

THE DAVY FAMILY AND DAVY-BUILT
MERCHANT VESSELS

Exeter Flying-post 22 May 1772
This is to give notice that the partnership between Jos. Lee and James
Davy, of Topsham, limeburner, being dissolved, the said Jos. Lee hath
erected new kilns, and intends carrying on that business on his own
account, where he hopes to have the continuance of his friends favours.
NB. The kilns are now burning. Topsham, May 13, 1772.

Exeter Flying-Post 17 April 1783
Lime trade. To be lett for a term, and taken possession of immediately,
three complete lime-kilns, with three large walled yards adjoining, for
landing culm, coals, and an extensive quay, situated near Countess Wear in
the parish of Topsham, Devon [possibly the kilns at Gulpit later worked by
the Davys]. The tenant may be accommodated with an exceeding good
stone sloop and two lighters, at a reasonable price, or to employ them by the
year; also a large quantity of limestones, now on the quay, and in the
quarry. Likewise to be lett for the residue of a term, four years of which are
unexpired, two good limestone quarries, in excellent work, at Babicomb, in
the parish of Mary Church. For further particulars apply to Mr Lee jun. the
owner, at Countess Wear. April 16, 1783.

Exeter Flying-Post 7 March 1799
For Kingston, Jamaica, now lying at Topsham, the good ship *Grace*,
burthen 300 tons. An entire new vessel [built at Glasshouse, Countess
Wear, by Robert Davy], being just launched, copper fastened and
sheathed; mounts ten carriage guns, besides small arms. Is neatly fitted up
for the convenience of passengers, will sail the next convoy in March, and
can touch at any of the Western ports, if required. For freight, passage, and
other particulars, apply to James Tompson, the master, on board; or to Mr
Robert Davy, Topsham.
N.B. A respectable person is going out in the above vessel to settle at
Jamaica, and will be glad to transact business on the usual terms.
Dated 25th Feb. 1799

Exeter Flying-Post 28 March 1799
Exmouth. Sailed . . . *Grace*, Thompson, for Plymouth to join convoy for
Jamaica.

Trewman's Exeter Flying-Post 22 February 1816
For sale, now on the stocks, and ready for launching, a vessel of about 120
tons register, strong and faithfully built, copper-fastened, will carry a large
cargo, and sail well. For particulars apply to Robert Davy, Topsham.
Dimensions

	Ft.	in.
Length on deck	70	0
Extreme breadth	20	2
Depth of hold	12	4

Also, a vessel of about 80 tons register, ready for launching. Also, two other vessels of about 80 tons each, well adapted for the coasting or Newfoundland trade, ready for launching.

Trewman's Exeter Flying-Post January 29 and February 5, 1818
To be sold, the good schooner *Mary*, launched in March last, and fitted with every material of the very best quality. She is a strong handsome well-built vessel and wants nothing but provisions to send her to sea. Admeasures about 86 tons, and is well calculated for general purposes. Applications to Robert Davy, ship-builder, Topsham. January 28th, 1818.

Trewman's Exeter Flying-Post 1 April 1819
To sail direct for St John's, Newfoundland, the good schooner *Plenty*, now lying at Topsham Quay, and will be dispatched in five or six days: Has room for a few tons of goods. For freight or passage, apply to Mr William Tozer, Topsham. Topsham, 31st March 1819.

Trewman's Exeter Flying-Post 14 August 1828
For sale. By auction at the Globe Inn, Topsham, in the county of Devon, on Wednesday, the 20th instant August, by four o'clock in the afternoon, the schooner *Plenty*, now lying at Topsham. Burthen per register, 87 tons, and carries a large cargo. Built by Mr Robert Davy at Topsham, in 1805, and rebuilt by him in 1816, for the Newfoundland trade; sails fast, and shifts without ballast, and may be sent to sea at a trifling expence. W. Carlisle, auctioneer, Topsham, August 8th, 1828

Trewman's Exeter Flying-Post 15 November 1821
To be sold by public auction on Saturday, December 1st, 1821, at the Salutation Inn, Topsham, at five o'clock precisely, unless previously disposed of by private contract, the good sloop *Active*, A1, $67^{57}/_{94}$ tons per register; built at Topsham for private use; is extremely well found in all kind of useful stores, and would require little outfit, excepting provisions, to send her to sea; she sails fast and carries a large cargo for her tonnage, is well adapted for general purposes. For particulars, &c apply to Mr Danl B. Davy of Topsham.

Trewman's Exeter Flying-Post 26 January 1826, Exeter column dated 25 January
Died . . . Yesterday [24 January], suddenly in the Defiance coach between Exeter and Newton Bushell, on his journey to Plymouth, Mr Thos. Bishop, of Topsham, former shipwright to Mr Robert Davey, in whose employ he has been for upwards of forty years, a truly industrious, honest and faithful man. [Aged 70 years, buried at Topsham on 28 January 1826: Topsham parish register.]

Trewman's Exeter Flying-Post 21 July 1831
A fine schooner, of 150 tons, named the *Postboy*, was launched from the building yard of Messrs Davey, Topsham, on the 12th inst.

Trewman's Exeter Flying-Post 10 December 1835
Lime trade. To be let, and may be entered on at Christmas next, a set of lime kilns, desirably situated adjoining the River Exe, at Lympstone, where the lime trade has been carried on for many years past by Mr Davy. At the same time the stone boat and lighters which supply the said kilns, may be taken at a valuation. For particulars apply to Mr Stogdon, solicitor, Palace Street, Exeter.
[Further advertised 28 January 1836, 'may be entered on immediately'.]

Woolmer's Exeter & Plymouth Gazette 13 March 1841
On Tuesday morning [9 March], at half-past 7 o'clock, upwards of 2,000 persons were assembled in the building yard of D. B. Davy, Esq., at Topsham, to witness the launch of the splendid new barque *Emelyn*. On the occasion all the workmen employed were regaled at Southcott's Nelson Inn with a good substantial dinner.

Trewman's Exeter Flying-Post 19 August 1874
[Died] August 16, at Grove Hill, Topsham, D. B. Davy, Esq., aged 75.

Richards's Weekly Advertiser for Topsham and the surrounding district, No 58, Saturday, 22 August 1874
On Sunday morning Daniel Bishop Davy Esq., of Grove Hill, was summoned from our midst by the hand of death, the event being made known by the solemn tolling of the bell between seven and eight in the morning. Mr Davy had been in precarious health for some time past and his decease was not altogether unexpected. His removal will be much felt in many directions not only as a magistrate and a member of the school board, but as a friend and clear-headed counsellor to the poor, to whom he was always open cheerfully and willingly to lend his aid. The funeral took place this day (Friday) at twelve o'clock in the Topsham cemetery. The deceased was carried from his residence on a bier, no carriages being in attendance. A very large number of the tradesmen, farmers, &c, of that town and neighbourhood were present, and the shops were partially closed. The funeral service was conducted by the Rev. J. A. Leakey.

Appendix C

Contracts for building a stone boat of 74 tons and equipping her with sails, 1802: Devon Record Office, Rolle Estate Papers, 96M/Box 2/13.

Articles of agreement made, concluded and agreed upon this Fi[f]th day of Feb[r]uary One Thousand Eight Hundred and Two, between the Right Honourable Lord Rolle of the County of Devon & Thomas Owen, shipbuilder, Topsham, as follows:

The said Thomas Owen for himself, his heirs, executors, administrators & assigns doth covenant, promise & agree to build in a good and workmanlike manner a stone boat of 74 tons measurement for Lórd Rolle for and in consideration of the sum of seven hundred pounds, of scantlings and particulars as follows –

Keel in two pieces, sided 9 inches, mo[u]lded 12 ditto
Stem   ditto   ditto
Stern post sided and mo[u]lded at the wing transome 8 inches
Keelson sided and mo[u]lded 9 inches
Floor timbers sided 9 inches
First futtocks & second sided 7½ inches
Frame mo[u]lded at the floor heads 6 inches, at whale 5 in., at the gunwhale 4 inches.
2 whales 4 in. plank, black strake 3 in., bilge plank 3½ in., one inside and out 3 in. – from that to the keel 2½ in. elm, from belge [bilge] to the whale 2 in. oak plank
Clamps 2½ in. oak, bilge plank 2½ in. ditto, all the rest of the ceiling 2 in. oak plank

The said Thomas Owen to find and provide for the stone boat, one mast, bowsprite, boom & gaff, squaresail yard and a boat, and anchors suitable for her size, ironwork for the rigging, and to launch the said vessell on or before the 10th day of May Eighteen Hundred & Two

[Signed] Thos Owen

I Thomas Owen Junr, sailmaker, Topsham, do promise and agree to equip a stone boat for my Lord Rolle with 1 mainsail, 1 foresail, 2 jibbs and 1 squaresail with materials of the best quality, compleat for the sum of eighty pounds, dated this 5th day of February Eighteen Hundred and Two

[Signed] Thomas Owen Junr

[An entry in the Exeter Customs House Register of Shipping, Vol. 1 (1786–1811), 1802 No 35, suggests that this vessel was the *Bicton* of Exeter, registered on 3 July 1802, and described as a square-sterned sloop with a high quarter deck and one mast, built at Topsham that year. Her owner was John Rolle, Baron Rolle of Stevenstone, Devon, and her principal dimensions were as follows: length 54 ft 3½ in.; breadth 18 ft 5 in.; depth of hold 6 ft 3½ in.; 75 $^{64}/_{94}$ tons. John Phillips, her first master, was succeeded by Richard Hore, but the vessel was then lost. Another sloop with the same name was built by Robert Davy about 1812.]

Appendix D

The schooner *Ebenezer*: Agreement between Captain John Holman and others with her builder Daniel Bishop Davy, in latter's handwriting, 7 November 1827. Topsham Museum.

Memorandum of agreement for building a new vessell

Memorandum of agreement between John Holman and others on the one part and Mr D. B. Davy on the other part. John Holman and others agree for the said Mr D. B. Davy to build a new vessell agreeable to the following particulars – Length aloft 67 ft, length for measurement 64 ft 6 in., length of keel 59 ft, extreme breadth 19 ft, depth in the hold 11 ft, keel sided 10 in., moulded 13½ in., floors sided in midships 10½ in., moulded 11 in., first futtocks sided a midships 9 in., second ditto 8½ in. at the heel, and 7½ in. at the head, top timbers 7 in. sided, moulded at the head 4¾ in., at the bends 6 in., at the floor heads 8 in., stem sided 9 in., stern post 10 in. head, 9 in. at heel, to have a sufficient number of transims and a propertionable size, agreeable to the other part of the frame, paint strake 3½ in. thick, 9 in. wide, bends 4½ in. thick, 7 in. wide, and three in number, one strake above and below the main whales 3½ in. thick, three topside strakes 5 in. wide, 2½ in. thick, bilge strakes three in number 5 in. thick, 9 in. wide of good elmn, one strake above 3½ in. thick and one below of 4 in. thick good elmn, plank between the bilge strake and strake under the bends to be of 2½ English oak, plank on the bottom from the bilge strake to the keel to be of 3 in. elmn, clamps or stringers under the deck to be 6 in. thick and 9 in. wide, to have two strakes of 3½ in. thick, 7 in. wide abreast of the bends, bilge strakes on the floor heads three in number 3½ in. thick, 7 in. wide, limber strakes 3½ in thick, 10 in. wide, and all the rest of the sealing plank above the bilge strakes to be of 2½ oak, and below between the bilge strak[e]s and limber strake to be 3 in., kelson sided 12 in., moulded 13 in., beams 15 in number 10 in. sided, 9 in. moulded, knees sided 6½ in., waterways 5 in. thick, 10 in. wide, to be gruv'd and moulded 4 inches from the plank share, and to be copper fasten[e]d through the clamps or stringers, plank share 2½ in. thick to be fasten[e]d to the paint strake and waterway with ½ in. bolts, the plank each side the comings of oak 3½ in. thick, between the two oak plank a midships to be fill[e]d with 3½ oak well season[e]d, all the rest of the deck to be of the best Dantzic or Norway timber, six inches wide, 2½ ins thick, the whole of which to be fasten[e]d with 6 in. width copper nails on the beams and 5 in. on the carlings, comings round the mast, and pumps to be 4 in. thick and 7½ in. wide allowing them to be 3½ above the deck, the comings of the main hatchway to be lined with iron & also the beams and fore and aft carlings, the fore hatch to be tongued and made water taught, the after hatches two in number to be tongued and fitted with a shute in the

84

middle and made water taught, the winch bits fore and aft to be kneed to the deck, the rails round the stanchions to be 6½ in. wide and 3½ in. thick reeded out and in and in of the best red deal or oak, to find oak rails for belaying pins, fore and aft, oak channels with lower dead eyes and chain plates of the best iron, oak windlass 14 in. through with patent palls, chock and all necessary iron work belonging thereto for two chain cables, the double winch complete, four gudgeons on the rudder and four on the stern post, with a two inch bolt from top to bottom through the gudgeons, to fix a figure head with rails &c complete, owners finding the figure, the fore beam of the cabin and after beam of the forcastle deck to be kneed with small iron knees, to fit up a neat mahogany cabin and sufficient bed cabins in the forcastle with a trunk thro' the deck leading thereto for a chain cable, the bulkheads fore and aft to be tongued, to find catheads, ships and boats davits with all necessary iron work complete, all ring bolts and eye bolts in the deck sides and stanchions necessary for lashing goods &c, one wash strake 5 in. wide, 1½ in. thick, bullworks of the best red deal five strakes in number 5 in. wide, 1 in. thick, to be rabbeted and beaded, a skylight with wood grating complete, a companion & binnacle of good season[e]d deal, to be copper fasten[e]d and iron fast[en]ing to be used within 4 ft each way of the binnacle, scaffs [scarfs] of the keel, stem and all other fastenings under the bends to be of copper, the thick strakes on the bilge to be cross bolted in such a way as for every frame to receive a bolt, one iron knee each side on the upper transim or wing transim and to be sufficiently fasten[e]d, the kelson to be fasten[e]d through every floor and through the keel with 1¼ in. iron bolts, to have four breast hooks under the deck, one 11 ft sided 9 in., one 10 ft sided 8½ in., two 9 ft sided 8 in., one breast hook above the deck, all the plank and timber used about the said vessell to be of good English oak except where it is specifically mention[e]d to be otherwise, to find the leading chocks on the taffle [taffrail?], oak pumpwell and all leading and belaying cleats necessary about the hull, to find two boats, one of 16 ft long and one of 13 ft with 4 ash oars, 2 paddles, rudders, tillers & boat davits, the oak plank on the outside to be burnt instead of boil[e]d, and the whole to be fitted in a complete workmanship manner without any extr[aordinar]y charge whatever about the hull for the sum of £11 10s per ton, payments to be made as follows: one third when the keel, floors, stem and stern are up and one third when the timbers are in and the bends work'd and one third when the said vessel is complete and del[ivere]d in safety.

It is further agreed that the throat bolts of the breast hooks, transims, also the fastenings thro' the dead wood and gripe be of iron, the floors in midships to be 15 ft long and not to be more than 12 inches apart, and all her wooden ends to be fasten[e]d with dumps, and the plank from the bends down to the garboard to be double treenail'd in every timber, the said vessell to be completed and launch'd on or before the 20th June 1828. Penalty for non performance of this agreement £150.

[Signed] John Holman
Tho Paine

Witness Richd Treatt

We the undersign'd agree to be answerable to Mr D. B. Davy and other tradesmen agreed to by John Holman for such a proportion of the within mention'd vessell as we have hereunto set our hands this 7th day of November 1827

Charles Wills	one eighth
J & S Holman	⅜th
Tho Paine	⅔th
Danl B. Davy	⅛th
Wm Smack	⅛th
	⁸⁄₈

[This vessel was first registered at Exeter, her home port, as the *Ebenezer* on 11 September 1828. Her master was John Holman and she was a carvel-built, square-sterned schooner of 108 ³⁶⁄₉₄ tons 'burthen', with two masts, one deck, a standing bowsprit and 'a male bust-head'. The Customs House measurements, differing slightly from the contract, were recorded as follows: length 68 ft 8½ in., breadth taken below the main wales 19ft 2½ in., depth in the hold 11ft 4 in. and keel for tonnage 55 ft 2 in. 9 pts. Her owners were John Holman of Topsham, mariner, with 16 of her 64 shares, Thomas Paine of Topsham, merchant, with 16, and Charles Wills of Exeter, plasterer, Daniel Bishop Davy of Topsham, shipbuilder, Gilbert Henry Yarde of Topsham, gentleman, and William Smack of Honiton, merchant, with 8 shares each. A note in the shipping register adds: 'Custom House, Exeter, 30 October 1828 – John Holman, mariner, has transferred by bill of sale dated this day eight sixty-fourth shares to Sarah Holman, widow, both of Topsham, Devon' (Devon Record Office: Exeter Customs House Register of Shipping, Vol. 5 (1825–29), 1828 No 21). Sarah Holman was the widow of John Holman's father, Thomas, for whom the *Fortitude* was originally built. Plate 10 shows a painting of the *Ebenezer* at Malta, c. 1830.]

GLOSSARY

The definitions given here are taken mainly from *A Treatise on Marine Architecture* published in 1830 by Peter Hedderwick, designer of some of the vessels built in Robert Davy's yards for Scottish owners (see Introduction). Other sources are *A Dictionary of Sea Terms* by A. Ansted, compiled in 1897 and some of the works quoted in that volume, namely, W. Falconer, *An Universal Dictionary of the Marine* (1769), W. H. Smyth, *The Sailor's Word Book* (1867) and W. T. Brande and G. W. Cox (eds), *Dictionary of Science Literature and Art*, 3 vols, 1865–7 edn. The definitions are given as they appear in these works, written when wooden sailing ships were still being built and sailing in the seas off Devon. The *Shorter Oxford English Dictionary*, 1933 edition, has also been consulted. The terms relate principally to shipbuilding and not to boatbuilding.

⊠. The symbol for the broadest frame in a ship. See *Dead-flat*.

After-body. 'Every part of the ship which is abaft the midship section' (Hedderwick).

Ballast. 'Any heavy material, such as sand, stones, or iron, &c placed in the bottom of the vessel, to lower the centre of gravity and make the vessel stable, so as not to be easily canted or heeled over by the impulse of the winds or waves' (Hedderwick).

Banker. 'A vessel employed in the cod fishery, on the Banks of Newfoundland' (Ansted).

Beams. 'Large pieces of timber extending from one side of the vessel to the other, for binding her together and supporting the deck. The midship-beam is the beam immediately at the midship frame' (Hedderwick).

Bends. 'A general term for the main-wales. These are thick planks put round the outside of the vessel' (Hedderwick).

Bilge. 'The outer part of a ship's bottom, on which she rests when aground.'
  Bilge-pieces. 'Planks or keels fastened on the bilge of the vessel, for strengthening that part which rests on the ground' (Hedderwick).

Bitts. 'Small posts or timber heads fixed through the deck of a vessel, either round masts or at the foot of the bowsprit. There are various bitts in a ship, but in small craft the term is generally understood to mean the *bowsprit bitts*, which support the stock of the bowsprit and frequently serve as kevels, or cleats, around which to 'bitt' or wind the cable, so that it shall remain fast. In large vessels we find *riding bitts*, which are stout heads rising considerably from the deck expressly for the purpose of 'bitting' the cable' (Ansted).

Black-strake. 'The strake on a vessel's side which is made black' (Ansted). 'A range of planks immediately above the wales in a ship's side; they are always covered with a mixture of tar and lamp-black, which preserves the plank itself and forms an agreeable variety with the white bottom beneath, and the scraped planks of the side, covered with melted turpentine, or varnish of pine, alone' (Falconer).

Bolts. 'Pieces of iron or copper, in the form of pins, which fasten two pieces of timber together. *Ring-bolts* have an iron ring of about 3, 4, or 5 inches in diameter, passing through an eye or opening in one end of the bolt; when the bolt has merely an eye, and no ring, then it is called simply an *eye-bolt*. The ring-bolts are much used in shipbuilding. A few are fixed in the ship's deck or stanchions, for lashing the boats, or any other thing, down to the deck; the eye-bolts are also fixed in various parts of the hull, for hooking tackle, or fastening ropes to' (Hedderwick).

Bomb. 'A small war-vessel carrying mortars for throwing bombs. More fully bomb-ketch, bomb-vessel, etc.' (*Shorter Oxford English Dictionary*).

Breadth. 'The measure of a ship from side to side in any particular place. It is usually distinguished into extreme breadth, main breadth, and top-timber breadth' (Hedderwick).

Breasthooks. 'Large pieces of timber bolted across the inside of the ship's bow' (Hedderwick).

Brig. 'A vessel with two masts (fore and main), both of them square rigged, but having a gaff mainsail. The brig is [1897] becoming a rare vessel, the brigantine and schooner having taken its place to a great extent' (Ansted).

Brig-mast. 'The name given to a mast which carries a top-gallant mast, in contradistinction to the schooner-mast, which has no top-gallant, but only lower and top-mast. The brig-mast is the distinguishing difference between the brigantine and the schooner, and between the barquentine and the three-masted schooner' (Ansted).

Brigantine. 'A two-masted vessel, with a brig's fore-mast, square-rigged, and a schooner's main-mast, fore-and-aft rigged' (*Shorter Oxford English Dictionary*).

Bulwarks. 'Planks to defend the vessel against the violence of the waves or the assaults of an enemy' (Hedderwick). 'The raised woodwork running along the sides of a vessel above the level of the deck' (*Shorter Oxford English Dictionary*).

Buttock. 'A part of the vessel near the stern, about the surface of the water' (Hedderwick).

Cable. 'The rope or chain by which a ship's anchor is held' (Ansted).

Cant-timbers. 'Those timbers which are situated at the two ends of a ship. They derive their name from being canted or raised obliquely from the keel, in contradistinction to those whose planes are perpendicular to it' (Falconer). 'That which is placed in a canting or sloping position' (Hedderwick).

Carlings or *carlines.* 'Pieces of oak, about 4 or 5 inches square, let into the beams of the vessel at each end, so that they are straight with the upper side of the beams, and lie in a fore-and-aft direction. Between the carlings, are pieces which lie parallel with the beams, called *ledges*' (Hedderwick).

Carvel-built. 'Vessels or boats which have smooth bottoms, and whose planks are all flush, are said to be carvel-built, in opposition to those which have the edges of their planks overlapping each other, like the slates on a house, which are called clencher-built vessels' (Hedderwick).

Cat-head. 'A beam projecting at each side of the bows of a ship, for raising the anchor, or carrying it suspended' (*Shorter Oxford English Dictionary*).

Caulking. 'The operation performed upon wooden vessels to prevent leakage, and assist in fixing the whole frame of the hull. It consists of stuffing the seams (the spaces between the planks) with oakum, and then paying them with hot pitch' (Ansted).

Ceiling. 'The inside planks of a vessel' (Hedderwick).

Channels, main, fore, and mizzen. 'Pieces of timber or planks bolted edgeways to the ship's sides, in order to spread the rigging and carry it clear of the rail.' *Channel-wales.* 'Thick planks bolted around the inside of the vessel opposite the channels, in order to secure and strengthen the top sides of the vessel' (Hedderwick).

Chocks. 'Pieces of wood used for filling up any want or defect. At the joints of timbers cross-chocks are used; these scarph on to each timber, and connect the two together' (Hedderwick).

Clamps. 'Substantial planks put round the vessel on the inside of the timbers; the ends of the beams rest on them. The clamps are commonly bolted through every other timber of the side, and scarphed together with what is called hook-scarphs' (Hedderwick).

Clencher- (or *clinker-*) *built.* 'When the planks overlap each other at the edges, and form projections on the bottom. Clencher-built vessels are much stronger, in proportion to their weight, than carvel-built vessels' (Hedderwick).

Coamings. 'Pieces of wood raised round the sides and ends of the hatches, to prevent the water from running off the deck into the hold' (Hedderwick).

Companion. 'A raised hatch or cover to the cabin-stair of a merchant ship' (Hedderwick).

Crutch. 'Crooked timbers or iron bands bolted to the stern-post and sides of a vessel to unite these parts' (*Shorter Oxford English Dictionary*).

Cutwater. 'The foremost part of the ship's head, or main stem' (Hedderwick).

Dead-flat. 'The term [on shipbuilders' plans] for the midship bend; it is always distinguished by this mark ⊠; all the other frames or sections are distinguished by figures, or letters of the alphabet' (Hedderwick).

Deadwood. 'Certain large pieces of timber fitted on the keel at the stem and stern-post, for the purpose of raising the floor-timbers and bolting the heels of the cant-timbers' (Hedderwick).

Depth in the hold. 'One of the principal dimensions of a ship. For merchant vessels the depth in the hold is taken from the underside of the main-deck plank, at ⊠ frame, to the upper side of the ceiling-plank next the limbers' (Hedderwick).

Dump. 'A bolt or nail used in shipbuilding (also dump-bolt, dump-nail)' (*Shorter Oxford English Dictionary*).

Fair. 'Not suddenly crooked. A fair curve is one having no quirked or flat parts in it' (Hedderwick).

False keel, false stem, false stern-post, or the like. 'An additional keel, stem, or stern-post, fixed on the main keel, main stem, or main stern-post, to increase their strength, and make a ship hold a better wind' (Hedderwick).

Fashion pieces. 'The aftermost timbers of a vessel which form or 'fashion' the shape of her stern' (Ansted).

Floor. 'The bottom of a vessel near midships. In the midship body, the flattest part of the floor is at the flat frame marked ⊠. ' *Floor-guide*. 'A ribband which runs round a vessel, a little below the floor-heads' (Hedderwick). *Floor-head*. 'The upper end of one of the floor-timbers in a vessel' (*Shorter Oxford English Dictionary*). *Floor-ribband*. 'A diagonal ribband which is run round a vessel, a little below the floor-heads.' *Floor-timbers*. 'Large and strong pieces of timber which extend across the keel; upon these floors the frames are erected' (Hedderwick).

Foothook. See *Futtock*.

Fore and Aft. 'Opposite terms. In speaking of any plank, or thing, which is lying towards the bow and stern end of a ship, and not in a cross direction to her length, it is said to by lying fore and aft' (Hedderwick).

Fore-body. 'Every part of the hull before ⊠, i.e. the dead-flat frame; and the *After-body* is the hull abaft of the same' (Hedderwick).

Fore-rake. 'So much of the forward inclination, or run, of the stem of a vessel as overhangs the keel' (Ansted).

Frame of timbers. 'In shipbuilding, signifies a number of pieces of timber bolted together, in order to form the bottom and sides of a vessel. It consists in a large vessel of the floor-timber, two first futtocks, two second futtocks, two third futtocks, two fourth futtocks, and one or two long and short top-timbers on a side. The frames are placed at right angles to the keel' (Hedderwick).

Full. See *Lean*.

Futtock. 'This term is evidently derived from the lowest part, or foot, of a timber, and from the hooked shape of the piece; hence *foothook* (a hook in shipbuilding, being anything bent or incurvated). In shipbuilding, a futtock is one of the members composing the ribs of a vessel. The ribs of large ships cannot be made of one piece, as can those of open boats; they consist, therefore, of several or members, scarfed together, each one being called a 'futtock'. The lowest of these is the floor-timber, also called the ground futtock or (amidships) the navel futtock; the one above it is the second futtock; above that, if there be one, the third futtock; and the top futtock is the top timber' (Ansted).

Garboard-strake. 'A course of the outside bottom plank next the keel of the ship' (Hedderwick).

Gripe. 'The fore foot or fore end of the keel of a ship on which the stem is set; or, in other words, the sharpness of her stem under water; which is made thus to gripe the water' (Ansted).

Gunwale (pronounced 'gunnel'). 'A plank or wale which runs round the vessel's upper works, a little above the deck. In merchant ships it is called the covering-board, as it lies on the ends of the top timbers, and the stanchions which support the rail pass through it. The gunwale is also called the *plank sheer*' (Hedderwick).

Half-breadth. 'Is the distance measured from the centre line of the ship, to any of the sides. Half-breadth plane is a name for the floor-plane' (Hedderwick).

Hanging-knees. 'Those which have one of their arms vertical' (Hedderwick).

Harpings or *harpins.* 'In shipbuilding certain of the wales (planks) at the forward part of the hull are thicker than elsewhere: these stronger wales are called harpings' (Ansted).

Hatches. 'Openings in the deck through which any thing is lowered down into the hold. The fore-hatch is near the bow, the main-hatch is commonly in the middle of the ship, and the after-hatch is abaft the mainmast' (Hedderwick).

Heel. 'Is the lower end or bottom part of any thing, as the heel of a timber, the heel of a mast, the heel of a ship, that is, the keel and stern-post at the lower end. It also signifies the canting or inclining of a vessel from the perpendicular position' (Hedderwick).

Hoy. 'A small vessel, usually rigged as a sloop, and employed in carrying passengers and goods, particularly in short distances on the sea-coast' (Smyth).

Hull. 'The sides, bottom, and deck of a vessel' (Hedderwick).

Keel. 'The principal piece of timber of a ship. It extends from the stem to stern-post and in a small vessel it may consist of one piece throughout. For those of a larger size, the keel is formed of two or three pieces, which are scarphed together, and laid on the blocks. The other timbers which compose the vessel are erected on it' (Hedderwick).

Keelson (pronounced and sometimes written *kelson*). 'An internal keel placed immediately above the floor-timbers, and bolted down through every other floor and the keel' (Hedderwick).

Ketch. 'A trading vessel with two masts, main and mizzen. Both these masts are fore-and-aft rigged, the mizzen with or without topsail; and there is, in addition, often a large lower square sail set on the mainmast. The ketch is, in fact, of all our coasting traders, perhaps the most capable of variety in its rig. It may set one, two, or even three square sails on the mainmast; as many as four head sails; and one or even two staysails between masts' (Ansted).

Knees. 'Pieces of timber in the form of a right angle; they are sometimes made of iron, and are used for binding the beams to the ship's sides, the one leg or arm of the knee being bolted to the side-timbers, and the other to the beam' (Hedderwick).

Knightheads. 'Two timbers bolted to the stem, between which the bowsprit is fixed; also called *bollard-timbers*' (Hedderwick).

Lean, or *Clean,* and *Full.* 'The first two signify that the ship is sharp; the second that she is not so' (Hedderwick).

Ledges. See *Carlings.*

Lighter. 'A boat, usually a flat-bottomed barge, used in lightening or unloading (sometimes loading) ships that cannot be wharfed, and for transporting goods in harbour, etc' (*Shorter Oxford English Dictionary*). Some of the River Exe lighters were ketch-rigged; others had a single mast and a lugsail.

Limbers. 'An opening between the bottom of the floor-timbers and the garboard-strake, making a passage to the pumps for the water which gathers in the ship' (Hedderwick).

Lines (in marine architecture). 'The drawings of the form or shape of the intended vessel. These drawings are three in number: 1. The sheer plan; 2, the half-breadth plan; 3, the body plan. The sheer plan is the side view on which are laid off the length, heights of all parts from the keel, etc. The half-breadth plan shows the horizontal or floor plan on any water line. The body plan is the end view showing the curves of the sides at any point in her length; and since the two sides are exactly alike, the left half represents the vertical sections in the after part of the body, and the right half those in the fore part, or vice versa. Thus, lines running parallel to the surface of the water (such as the water lines) appear as straight lines parallel to the keel in the sheer plan; as straight lines at right angles to the keel in the body plan, and as curved lines on the half-breadth plan' (Ansted).

Luff of the bow. 'The part near the cat-head' (Hedderwick).

Main breadth. 'The extreme breadth of the ship' (Hedderwick).

Masts. 'A long piece, or system of pieces, of timber, placed nearly perpendicularly to the keelson of a vessel to support the yards, or gaffs, on which the sails are extended. When a mast is one entire piece, it is called a *pole-mast*; but in all large vessels it is composed of several lengths, called *lower, top* and *top-gallant* masts – sometimes a fourth, called a *royal* mast, which, however, is usually in one piece with the top-gallant mast' (Brande and Cox). 'A mast is said, when set up, to be stepped, because its foot is fitted into a *step*, or chock, the office of which is to distribute the weight of the mast over as great a part of the keelson as may be possible. It is held upright to the level of the deck by a framework called the *mast-case*; and is further strengthened, on the deck itself, by a frame called the *partners*. The lower portion of the mast is usually square, this part being called the *housing*, because it is housed, or enclosed in the mast case' (Ansted).

Midships or *amidships.* 'The middle of the ship' (Hedderwick).

Moulds. 'Thin pieces of fir formed to the shape of the timbers. Moulds for drawing the plans of vessels are thin pieces of pear-tree, of different forms, such as parts of circles, ellipses, &c' (Hedderwick).

Nails. 'Iron pins for fastening one piece of wood to another; they are made of different forms and strengths, according to the purposes for which they are intended. A *spike-nail* is the largest kind, varying from 4 to 8 or 9 inches in length; *ribband-nails* are large round nails made with round heads – they are chiefly used for nailing the ribbands to the timbers, or nailing a cleat which requires to be taken off again; *clamp-nails* are short and thick, and are used for fastening iron plates or the like. The nails which are used for nailing down the deck-plank to the beams are made of copper and tin' (Hedderwick).

Oakum. 'The substance to which old ropes are reduced when unpicked. It is used in caulking the seams of vessels, and in stopping leaks etc.' (Ansted). Falconer gives *oakham* as an alternative spelling. *White oakum* is made from untarred rope.

Pawl-bitt. See *Windlass.*

Pitch. 'Tar boiled to a harder and more tenacious consistency. When cold, it is quite hard' (Hedderwick).

Plank-sheer. See *Gunwale*.

Pointer. 'Naut. (pl) Timbers sometimes fixed diagonally across the hold, to support the beams' (*Shorter Oxford English Dictionary*).

Quarter. 'The top sides of a vessel near the stern end' (Hedderwick).

Quarter-galleries. 'A kind of additional cabin projecting without the quarters of a vessel' (Hedderwick).

Rabbet, or *rebate*. 'A kind of V groove cut along the upper edge of the keel, for the purpose of receiving the edge or end of any planks that are to fit against it. There is a rabbet cut on each side of the after-edge of the main stem, and fore-edge of the main stern-post, into which the ends of the planks butt' (Hedderwick).

Rails. 'Any long narrow pieces of timber put around the deck at a convenient height, to prevent the crew from being washed overboard. The main-rail reaches from the stem to the stern; the *taffrail* is a continuation of the main-rail across the stern' (Hedderwick).

Ribbands. 'Planks bolted outside the ribs to give stability to them during the building of the vessel' (Ansted).

Rosin. 'The seams in the way of such parts of the ship as are to be painted, are commonly paid [payed] over with rosin, which is cleaner than pitch; but the pitch is preferable on all other counts, as it is found that the rosin rots the oakum, and very soon decays itself' (Hedderwick).

Scantling. The dimensions of the timbers making up the frame of a vessel. See *Sided and moulded*.

Scarfing (Scarphing). 'Joining two pieces of timber together, by overlapping the end of one piece over the other, but having both points thinned off, so that when joined they appear as an even surface' (Hedderwick).

Sheathing. 'Thin boards or sheets of copper nailed on the bottom of a vessel, to protect it from [wood-gnawing teredo] worms' (Hedderwick). Later in the nineteenth century ships were felted and yellow-metalled. For a description of how this was done see Basil Greenhill, *The Merchant Schooners*, 1968 edn, vol. 1, pp. 112–3.

Sheer. 'The curve or bend downwards in the middle of the top-sides, or upper-works of a vessel' (Hedderwick).

Sheer plan. See *Lines*.

Sheer-plank, sheer-strake, or *paint-strake*. 'Broad strakes of plank put round the vessel at the top of the timbers. They are commonly thicker than the other planks of the top-sides. On the lower edge of the paint-strake, a moulding is formed, corresponding with that on the edge of the gunwale or plank-sheer' (Hedderwick).

Sided and *moulded*. 'The siding-dimension is the breadth of the timbers; moulding-dimension is their thickness' (Hedderwick).

Sirmark. 'A mark made on the moulds of the timbers, to distinguish the spot where the bevel is to be applied in bevelling the timbers' (Hedderwick).

Sloop. 'According to the general acceptation of the word, a small merchant or coasting vessel with one mast. But all ships of the Royal Navy carrying less than twenty guns, and being above the class of gun-vessels, are denominated sloops, excepting bomb-vessels and fire-ships' (J. W. Norie, *The Shipwright's Vade-Mecum*, 1822, p. 132).

Smack. 'A small vessel commonly rigged as a sloop or hoy, used in the coasting or fishing trade; or as a tender in the King's service' (Falconer).

Snow. 'A snow is the largest two-masted vessel, and is extremely convenient for navigation. The sails and rigging on the main and fore mast are similar to those on the same masts in a ship, the braces of the sails on the main-mast leading forward: besides which, there is a small mast, close behind the main-mast, that carries a trysail, resembling the mizen of a ship. The mast, called the trysail-mast, is fixed by an iron clamp to the aft-side of a chock in the trestle-trees. An *hermaphrodite* is a vessel so constructed as to be, occasionally, a snow, and sometimes a brig' (Steel's *Art of Rigging*, 1818, p. 122).

Square. 'A piece of timber is said to be square when its sides form right angles to each other' (Hedderwick).

Stanchion or *Stantion*. 'An upright post in the frame of a ship. Certain stanchions support the beams in a vessel, others are to be found along the bulwarks. The small posts sometimes seen running round the gunwale of a launch, yacht, or part of a deck, and supporting a man rope, are also called stanchions' (Ansted).

Standards. 'Large iron knees fitted between the beams of the upper and 'twixt-decks, bolted to these beams and the ship's side. They are sometimes called iron staple-knees' (Hedderwick).

Stem. 'The principal timber which forms the bow of the vessel, into which the ends of the bow plank are fixed' (Hedderwick).

Stern-post. 'A strong piece of timber, generally extending from the keel to the upper deck. It fits to the after end of the keel with mortise and tenon, and is fastened by the deadwoods and heel-knee. The *inner stern-post* is fitted to the fore side of the main stern-post and generally extends from the keel to the under side of the wing transom' (Hedderwick).

Strake (often pronounced 'streak'). 'A strake is a line of planking extending the length of a vessel' (Ansted). See *Black-strake, Garboard-strake, Sheer-plank* and *wales*.

Stringers. 'Strakes of planks wrought around the inside at the height of the underside of the beams. They are bolted to the clamps and timbers, and are hook-scarphed. As they are put on edgeways, and serve as a shelf to rest the beams upon, they are sometimes called shelf-pieces' (Hedderwick).

Superficial. Square measure of timber, distinct from linear and solid.

Room and space. In the frame of a ship, the distance from the side of one timber to the same side of the next; 'or the distance from moulding edge to moulding edge; it is always 1½ or 2 inches greater than the breadth or siding dimension, and can never be less.' Also called timber and room, room and timber, or birth and space. (Hedderwick).

Taffrail. See *Rails*.

Timber. 'All timber is bought and sold by the load, and a load is 50 feet, which is supposed to weigh a ton, or 20 hundred weight; but some reckon 40 feet of rough or unhewn timber to the load; for they say, that, as hewn timber is measured by the square, it is very nearly exact; but rough timber, being measured by the girt (or quarter compass,) which is more than one-fifth less than exact, therefore, in the buying and selling of timber, it amounts to much the same, whether it is measured to the girt, at 40 feet solid to the load, or measured exactly at 50 feet to a load, the price being in proportion. In the King's yards 40 feet of hewn timber is reckoned a ton, and 50 feet of such timber goes to a load' (J. W. Norie, *The Shipwright's Vade-Mecum*, 1822, p. 65).

Top-timbers. 'Timbers forming the top-sides' (Hedderwick).

Transoms. 'Large pieces of timber which lie horizontally across the stern-post, and form the buttock; they are bound together at the end by a timber called the *fashion-timber*' (Hedderwick).

Treenails. 'Cylindrical oak pins driven through the plank and timbers to fasten them together' (Hedderwick).

Trim of a vessel. 'The proper adjusting of the sails or cargo' (Hedderwick).

Tumble home, fall home, and *tumbling in.* 'Terms used to describe the inward curve from the bilge upward, peculiar to certain vessels. In the old battleships [wooden walls] this was particularly noticeable. The continuation of this curve below the water-line and towards the keel is sometimes called the *flare*, which name is also applied to the outward curve of the bows' (Ansted).

Unfair. See *Fair.*

Wales. 'The principal strakes of thick plank, wrought round the outside of a vessel, about the load-water mark. They are sometimes called the bends' (Hedderwick).

Water-line (in Naval architecture). 'A section of the hull, taken parallel to the line of flotation. There are two cardinal ones; the *water-line* or *light water-line*, and the *load water-line*. The first is the line to which a vessel is designed to float; the second that down to which she may with safety be immersed when freighted. And between these two there may be, for purposes of calculation in the designing of a vessel, any number of water-lines. In the popular sense the water-line of a boat is the line of flotation' (Ansted).

Waterways (in a ship). 'The deck planks extending round the ship's sides, and usually having grooves or channels which carry off the water from the decks' (Ansted).

Whelps. 'Pieces of wood or iron bolted on the windlass, to save the main piece from being chafed by the cable' (Hedderwick).

Windlass. 'A strong piece of wood turning round on an iron spindle, which is fixed into its ends; it lies in a horizontal position across the ship, and is turned round by levers, called hand-spikes' (Hedderwick).

Wing-transom. 'The uppermost of the main transoms' (Hedderwick).

A note on tonnage

The method of measuring a ship's tonnage was changed several times during Daniel Davy's lifetime, but 'Old measurement' or 'Builders' measurement' was the system in force when most of the entries were made in the Memoranda Book. The following method of estimating it when a vessel was laid dry is given in an 1826 edition of Nesbit and Little's *Treatise on Practical Gauging*:

> Measure the length on a straight line along the rabbit [rabbet] of the keel of the ship, from the back of the main stern-post, to a perpendicular line let fall from the fore-part of the main stem, under the bowsprit; from this length, subtract ⅗ of the extreme breadth; and the remainder will be the length of the keel for tonnage. The breadth must be taken from outside to outside of the plank, in the broadest part of the ship, whether above or below the main wales, exclusive of all manner of doubling planks, or sheathing, that may be wrought upon the sides of the vessel; then multiply the length of the keel, in feet, by the breadth, and this product by half the breadth; divide the last product by 94; and the quotient will be the tonnage required.

The authors also give a method of estimating the tonnage when a vessel was afloat. The formula for 'Builders' measurement' described above was as follows:

$$\frac{(L - \tfrac{3}{5}B) \times B \times \tfrac{1}{2}B}{94}$$

A monograph by the late Grahame Farr entitled *Shipbuilding in North Devon* (National Maritime Museum, 1976) includes a summary of the various Acts of Parliament relating to the tonnage of ships. The whole subject is described as a nightmare.

INDEX

Science Museum, London, xxv; library, xvi
'Scotch smacks', *see* Smacks, Leith-London
Scott & Sons, John, Greenock shipbuilders, vii, 13
Scott, William, Greenock, Barnstaple and Bristol, 13
Scovell, John and Henry, wharfingers, 34
Sellick (or Silleck), Mr, Newcastle, 12, 20
Sherlock, William, Monkwearmouth, timber agent, 12, 20; prices obtained by, 21
Shipbuilding:
   Contracts, xix, xxi, xxvi, 71, 83–6
   Materials and costs, xviii, xix, xxi, xxvi, 24–45; at Bridport, 13–14; Dartmouth, 22; Greenock, 13; Hull, 15–18; Hythe, 15; Lynn, 15; Redbridge, 14; Weymouth, 14. *See also* Timber trade
   Plans, viii, ix
   Terms, viii, ix. *See* Glossary, 87–95
Ships, full-rigged, ix, Plates 1 and 4
   Estimate for building one of 430 tons, 25–7
   Exe-built, xxiv–xxv, 58, 59, 80
   Three launched at Greenock, 13
   Under construction at Hull, 15, 16
Ships' names
   Ace of Trumps, xiv, xviii, xx, xxix, 60
   Active, galliot, 2, 59
   Active sloop (or smack), 59, 61, 67; for sale, 81
   Adder 1805, xxiii
   Adder 1813, xxii, xxiii, 58, 70, 79
   Agenoria, 59
   Albion brig, 59
   Albion schooner, 58
   Albion ship, 13
   Alert galliot, 2, 59
   Alert smack 1807, 58
   Alert smack 1817, 59
   Alexander, 23
   Amy, xiv, 60
   Anacreon, xxiii
   Ann, x, 58
   Arcade, 59
   Archibald, 59, 70
   Armada, xxiii
   Barley Mow, 61
   Batavia (ex-*Caroline*), x, xxiv, 58, 70; painting of, viii, 70, Plate 1
   Bedford, 78
   Bee, xvii, xxviii, 59; detailed dimensions, 46–7
   Beelzebub, xxiii
   Belle Alliance, 23
   Betsey, ix, 61
   Bicton 1802, 83
   Bicton 1812, 59, 83
   Black Cat, xx
   Brisk, xxiii
   Brissett, 59, 70
   Bristol Packet, 58

Ships' names—*cont.*
   Britannia 1815, 59
   Britannia 1822, xiv, xx, 60; materials and costs, 40–41
   British Fair, 77
   Brothers, 59
   Bustler, xxiii
   Caledonia, 23
   Camel, 78
   Carnation, xxiii
   Caroline, armed brig, 78
   Caroline, East Indiaman, *see Batavia*
   Cephalus, 58
   Ceres, xi, xxvi, xxvii, 4, 8, 15, 59, 60, 61, 67
   Cheerly, 78, 79
   City of Exeter, xxvii
   Clarence, xxiii
   Clinker, xxii, xxiii, 58, 79
   Clitus, viii, xv, 60
   Come On, xx
   Comet, xxiii
   Commerce, 61
   Commodore, xxvii
   Conflict, x, xxiii, 58, 70
   Conqueror, 61
   Constitution, U.S.S., xxi
   Coquette, xx
   Cracker, 79
   Cyane, xxi, xxiii, 78
   Cynthia, 58, 59
   Cyrene, xxiii
   Czar, xvi, 59
   Daphne, xxiii, 58, 71, 78
   Darby Allen, 67
   Dartmouth, xxiii
   Defiance, 61
   Delight, xxiii
   Derwent, xxiii
   Dorothea, xiv, xxviii, 8, 60; detailed dimensions, 51–4; masts and yards, 10
   Dove, 2, 59
   Duniere, 61
   Eagle, xvi, xvii, 59
   Earl St Vincent, x, xxiv, 58, 70; under construction, 76
   Ebenezer, viii, xiv, xxi, 60, Plate 10; original contract, 84–6
   Eclipse, xxvi, 7, 60, 61; materials and costs, 29–31
   Edinburgh Castle, xvi, xvii, xix, 7, 60; materials and costs, xix, 27–9
   Elephant, 61
   Eliza lighter, 61
   Eliza schooner, xiv, xxviii, 8, 45, 60; detailed dimensions, 55–7
   Emelyn, xiv, 60; launch of, xv, 82
   Endeavour, xx
   England's Rose, xx
   Erebus, Pembroke-built, xxiii
   Erebus, Topsham-built, xxiii, 79

Timber, shipbuilding, xix, xxi. *See also*
Shipbuilding contracts, Shipbuilding
materials and costs and Timber trade.
Timber merchants, 12, 20, 21
Timber trade, vii, 13–21
Tonnage formula, 96
Toppings Wharf, Southwark, London, 34
Topsham, vii
Bridge, 72
Coal that will suit, 22; coal yard and
quay, xi
Follett's Quay and timber yard, xii, xiii
Furlong, xxviii
Grove Hill House, xv, 82
Land: 'measurement of parish' in 1839,
67; Robert and D. B. Davy's, 66
Lock opposite, 72
Marine stores, export of, xxvii
Maritime community, xxviii–xxix
Museum, viii, xiv, xxi, 69
Parish church, xi, 69, 70, 76
Parish registers, published in 1938, xi,
xxviii–xxix
Passage shipyard, vii, x, xxvi, xxviii;
description, xv; developed by Robert
Davy, 71; drawing of store, xiii; let to
Holman & Walters, xv; shown on plan
of riverside properties, xii; steam
engine used for sawing timber, xv–xvi
Post office accounts, 67
Privateer, 72–3
Public houses: Globe Inn, 81; Salutation
Inn, 81; Ship, xi; Southcott's Nelson
Inn, xv, 82, or Lord Nelson Inn, xi, 66,
74
Quay, 81
Shipbuilders, *see* Obadiah Ayles, John
Bishop, Thomas Bowden, Daniel
Davy, Robert Davy, Thomas Owen
and Tilney Rising
Ships, merchant, built there, ix, xiv, xv,
xvi, xvii, xviii, xix, xx, xxi, xxiv, xxv,
xxvi, xxvii, 2, 3, 4, 5, 6, 27, 33, 37, 40,
43, 59–60 (list), 71, 81, 82, 83–6;
warships, xi, xxi–xxiii, 58, 71, 77–9
Strand End shipyard, xxiv, xxvii
Strand graving dock and shipyard, xvi,
xxiv
Workhouse, 'nest of vice', 73
Torbay: limestone trade, xxvi, 7, 70
Torquay, 3
Tozer, William, 81
Treatt, Captain Richard Court, Exmouth,
33, 34, 85

Troake, —, 67
Turnchapel, near Plymouth: warships,
xxii, xxiii
Twyming, Mr, Southampton, 12, 21

Upton, William, Petworth, 12, 21

Vaudin, John, Guernsey, 22–3
Vickery, —, servant of Robert Davy, 75
Vines on lime-kiln walls, 76

Wales & Dobson, King's Lynn shipbuil-
ders, 11, 15
Walters, John, Exmouth shipbuilder, xx; &
Wishart, xx; & Holman, Topsham, xx,
xv
Walton, Thomas, Hull shipbuilder, 11, 16
Wapping, London, xvi
Ward, John, of Hull, marine artist, xvi,
xvii, Plates 6 and 7
Warnham, Sussex: timber merchant, 12, 21
Warships, vii, x, xi, xxi–xxiii, xxviii, 70, 71
Built on the Exe 1804–14 (newspaper
extracts), 77–9
Built in Devonshire merchant yards
1804–17, xxiii
Built by Robert Davy, 58
Wear, *see* Countess Wear
Webber, Captain Edward, 8
Well vessel, 59. *See also* Salmon
West Indiamen, x, xxiv, xxv, 70, 71, 76, 80,
Plate 4
Weymouth, 7, 34; shipbuilders, 14
Whalers, South Seas, xxiii
Whindfields & Thomas, Gateshead and
London, 15
Whitcombe, Thomas, marine painter, xxv,
Plate 4
White, Charles, London, 23
Whiteway, Joseph, shipowner, 3
Whiteway & Mudge, Torquay, 3
Wills, Charles, Exeter, 86
Wilson, George, Newcastle, 12, 20
Wimborne, Dorset: timber merchant, 12,
20, 21
Winch for raiding mainsail, xxvi, 4
Windlass, patent iron neck, 15
Wreford, William, 8
Wright, Harle & Co., South Shields, 18, 19

Yachts, xxvii, 5, 7, 60
Yarde, Gilbert Henry, Topsham, 86
Young, C., South Shields shipbuilder, 11,
18, 19